GARY LINEKER'S
SOCCER QUIZ BOOK

GARY LINEKER'S
SOCCER QUIZ BOOK

GARY LINEKER
WITH WILLIAM WALKER

CollinsWillow
An Imprint of HarperCollins*Publishers*

First published in 1992 by
CollinsWillow
an imprint of HarperCollins*Publishers*
London

Reprinted 1992

A CIP catalogue record for this book
is available from the British Library

ISBN 0 00 218436 2

Printed and bound in Great Britain

CONTENTS

Introduction   7

QUIZZES   9

British Football
1. The League Championship   9
2. Ups and Downs   11
3. The FA Cup   13
4. To Hull and Back   15
5. Scottish Football   17
6. The Football League Cup   19
7. In a Different League   21
8. Other Tournaments   23

Clubs and Players
9. Come On You Spurs   25
10. My Striking Partners   27
11. Soccer in the Midlands   29
12. The Captains   31
13. The Pride of Merseyside   33
14. Irish Cream   35
15. The Men Who Keep Them Out   37
16. Oh Gary, Gary…   39

International Soccer
17. Sweden '92 – the European Championship   41
18. World Cup '86   43
19. England's Lions   45
20. World Cup '90   47
21. European Championship '88   49
22. World Cup Qualifying   51
23. Best of British   53
24. World Cup – past history   55

Moves, Managers and Much More
25. The Managers   57
26. Have Boots – Will Travel   59

27. The Foreign Legion 61
28. Early Exchanges 63
29. You Are the Ref 65
30. 4-3-3 67
31. Dramatic Debuts 69
32. Super Subs 71

A Quiz for All Seasons
33. Quite a Season – 1991-92 73
34. Round the Grounds 75
35. Quite a Season – 1990-91 77
36. On The Spot 79
37. Quite a Season – 1989-90 81
38. Record Breakers 83
39. Quite a Season – 1988-89 85
40. Soccer – the World Game 87

European Football
41. The Champions' Cup 89
42. Futbol Español 91
43. Stars of Europe 93
44. The Cup-Winners' Cup 95
45. Calcio – the Italian League 97
46. The UEFA Cup 99
47. The French Connection 101
48. Continental Hit-Men 103

Soccer Trivia
49. Sporting Soccer Fans 105
50. Read All About It 107
51. Howzat! Footballing Cricketers 109
52. The Colours 111
53. You Must be Joking! 113
54. The Song Remains the Same 115
55. Soccer On The Box 117
56. Strange – but True? 119

ANSWERS 121

INTRODUCTION

Hi there! Everyone in football loves a challenge – whether its a striker like myself on the hunt for goals or a goalie striving to keep a clean sheet.

This quiz book will certainly challenge you on your football knowledge. You'll find over 1000 questions on a whole host of soccer topics – on tournaments from the World Cup to the Autoglass Trophy and on clubs from lowly Rochdale to mighty Real Madrid.

And just like the chances which fall to a striker, the questions come at you with varying degrees of difficulty. Each quiz is in three parts:

Open Goal (surely everyone must score here?)

Half-Chance (a bit more difficult)

Long-Range Shot (you'll need to be on form to put these away!)

You'll find also that there's a special *Sharp in the Box* teaser at the end of each quiz. That should really keep you on your toes!

The answers are all at the back but don't give up too easily. Remember, just as in striking, it's always worth having a speculative try!

Have fun…

GARY LINEKER

QUIZ 1
THE LEAGUE CHAMPIONSHIP

'I came very close to winning a Championship medal with Everton in 1986. While any team can win the cup, its invariably the best team that takes the League title.'

Open Goal

1. On April 26 1992, Liverpool's defeat of Manchester United confirmed Leeds as England's Champions. Where had Leeds themselves won 3-2 earlier that day?

2. How many Championships have Arsenal won under George Graham?

3. Which was the last team to win three consecutive League titles?

4. With which club did Peter Shilton win a Championship medal in 1978?

5. Who was Manchester United manager when the Reds last won the League Championship?

6. Can you name the Scot who skippered Leeds to the title in 1991-92?

Half Chance

7. Which team won the Championship by a record 13 points margin in 1985?

8. Who was the leading goalscorer for Aston Villa's successful side of 1981?

9. Two players appeared in every League match for Leeds

during 1991-92 – name either.

10. During the 1970s, a team won the Championship while on holiday in Majorca. Who were they?

11. The winners of the 1992 English Fourth Division were the First Division Champions of 1960. Which is the club in question?

12. In which decade did Sunderland last win the League title?

Long Range Shot

13. Which is the only team to have won the Championship while remaining undefeated?

14. How many times did Bob Paisley manage Liverpool to the title?

15. Who are the only post-war Champions to have won the title by winning less than half of their matches?

16. Which club enjoyed a three-in-a-row Championship success from 1924 to 1926?

17. In 1962, which team won the First Division Championship in what was their first-ever season in the top division?

18. Do you know which famous manager guided them to that triumph?

Sharp in the Box

Leeds United finished runners-up in the League Championship on five occasions between 1965 and 1972. Can you name the clubs who pipped them for the title?

QUIZ 2
UPS AND DOWNS

'While at Leicester, I experienced both promotion and relegation in successive seasons. Going up is definitely a better feeling than going down!'

Open Goal

1. Which club eventually lost its First Division place in 1992 after having been involved in relegation struggles in each of the previous four seasons?

2. Who won the 1992 Second Division play-offs?

3. Which team were relegated from Division One on the last day of the 1989-90 season but bounced back after just one season in the Second?

4. Which manager guided Ipswich to promotion as the 1992 Second Division Champions?

5. Which team played in the Second Division play-offs in four separate seasons between 1987 and 1992?

6. Whose goal in the Manchester derby of April 1974 helped confirm United's first relegation into Division Two for 37 years?

Half-Chance

7. Which team won promotion in 1991 after spending 17 consecutive seasons in Division Two?

8. Which was the first club to suffer automatic relegation from the Football League?

9. Who led Swindon Town to successive promotions in 1986

11

and 1987?

10. Which club plummeted from Division One to Division Four between 1984 and 1986?

11. In the 1987 First/Second Division play-offs, who beat Leeds in a replay to retain their top division status?

12. Which was the last team to win the First Division Championship in the season following promotion?

Long-Range Shot

13. In which year did the League introduce 'three up and three down' between Divisions One and Two?

14. Which club holds the record for Football League promotions?

15. What were the 19th century version of the play-offs called?

16. Which founder member club was forced to seek re-election to the Football League in 1986?

17. They dropped out of the First Division in 1992 and, in doing so, suffered a record 12th relegation. Who are they?

18. What was rather surprising about Manchester City's relegation in 1937-38?

Sharp in the Box

Can you name the four current Football League clubs which have never been relegated?

QUIZ 3
THE FA CUP

'Winning the FA Cup with Spurs was a real highlight of my career – it's every footballer's dream to play in a cup-winning team at Wembley.'

Open Goal

1. Which striker has scored more FA Cup Final goals than any other player?

2. Who was manager of Ipswich Town's FA Cup winning side of 1978?

3. Only one FA Cup Final has ended with a result of 3-3. Can you name the teams involved?

4. Which of Liverpool's successful 1992 team had been a semi-final loser with Arsenal in the previous season?

5. Who was the goalkeeper and captain of Wimbledon in 1988?

6. Which Second Division side did Liverpool defeat in the 1992 semi-finals?

Half-Chance

7. Can you name the manager who led QPR to Wembley in 1982?

8. Which Fourth Division team knocked Arsenal out of the 1992 competition?

9. Who scored an FA Cup Final winner against Everton in 1985 and later played for the Goodison Park club?

10. Which member of Sunderland's defeated side of 1992 had

been a loser on three previous occasions?

11. Which was the first top division team to go out of the FA Cup on a penalty shoot-out?

12. Since 1914, Liverpool have scored fifteen goals in ten FA Cup Final appearances. How many of them were scored in the first half?

Long-Range Shot

13. Which Arsenal defender committed an infamous 'professional foul' on West Ham's Paul Allen in the 1980 FA Cup Final?

14. Which team made history by arriving at Wembley by helicopter in 1983?

15. Who refereed the 1992 Final?

16. The rival managers in the 1973 Sunderland-Leeds Final had earlier been opponents as players in the Newcastle Manchester City match of 1955. Can you name them?

17. Since the war, only three teams have contested the FA Cup Final without a full international player in their ranks. Who were they?

18. Who is thought to be the only man ever to take the FA Cup trophy out of the UK?

Sharp in the Box

Five post-war Manchester United managers have led The Reds to an FA Cup Final. Name them.

QUIZ 4
TO HULL AND BACK

'Although the standard may not be as high as in the top flight, the lower divisions in England are every bit as fiercely contested.'

Open Goal

1. Which 66 year old Football League club folded in 1992?

2. Can you name the 1964 European Footballer of the Year who began his League career with Huddersfield Town?

3. Who is the former Norwich and Manchester City boss who managed Shrewsbury during 1991-92?

4. Which Cumbrian club, First Division table toppers at one stage of the 1974-75 season, finished bottom of the 1991-92 Football League?

5. At which club did both Kevin Keegan and Ray Clemence make their debut in professional football?

6. Which was the highest-placed Welsh club in the 1991-92 Football League?

Half-Chance

7. Can you name the Nigerian international who is Leyton Orient's most-capped player?

8. Which Yorkshire club have Dave Mackay, Lawrie McMenemy and Billy Bremner all managed?

9. The Third Division's longest serving members won promotion from that league in 1992. Can you name them?

10. Why are Chesterfield known as 'The Spireites'?

11. Colin Bell, who won 48 caps for England between 1968 and 1975, began his career at which small town Lancashire club?

12. Which Irish international striker netted 78 goals in 219 Football League outings for Gillingham between 1981 and 1987?

Long-Range Shot

13. Which team set a new record for consecutive seasons in Division Four between 1967 and 1985?

14. Who is the former Wimbledon manager who has been in charge of Crewe since 1983?

15. Dave Bamber's 28 League goals helped which seaside club win promotion via the play-offs in 1991-92?

16. Which is the largest city in England never to have staged top division football?

17. Which Cheshire club appointed a Uruguayan manager in 1989?

18. Which team won their first 13 League matches of 1985-86 and went on to clinch that season's Third Division Championship?

Sharp in the Box

Can you name the six British senior League clubs called 'Rovers'?

QUIZ 5
SCOTTISH FOOTBALL

'Scottish football seems to have a higher profile now as clubs there bring in big names to try to keep pace with Rangers.'

Open Goal

1. Scotland's top goalscorer in 1991-92 was also voted Footballer of the Year by both the Football Writers and the Scottish PFA. Who is he?

2. Which Edinburgh side won their first major trophy in 19 years when they beat Dunfermline in the 1991 Skol League Cup Final?

3. Who is the only Celtic manager never to have played for the club?

4. Which Scottish team made their debut in European competition during 1992?

5. What are the colours of Dundee United?

6. Can you name Glasgow's three Premier League clubs?

Half-Chance

7. Who, in February 1992, became the first Aberdeen manager to be sacked?

8. For which team did Manchester United boss Alex Ferguson once appear in a Scottish Cup Final?

9. Who were the 1992 Scottish First Division Champions?

10. Can you name the Middlesbrough defender who joined Celtic in November 1991?

11. The town of Paisley is home to which Scottish League club?

12. Who were the last pair of brothers to play together in a Scottish Cup winning team?

Long-Range Shot

13. Which provincial club won the Scottish League Championship in 1965?

14. Can you name the two Ukrainians who played for Rangers' 'Double' winning side of 1991-92?

15. What Scottish club does Jimmy Greaves profess to support?

16. Who is the only Hearts player to have won the Scottish Footballer of the Year award?

17. With which club did Charlie Nicholas win a Scottish Cup winners medal?

18. Name Ernie Walker's successor as secretary of the SFA.

Sharp in the Box

What are the four Scottish League clubs whose name begins with the letter 'C'?

QUIZ 6
THE FOOTBALL LEAGUE CUP

'Although it has never upstaged the FA Cup, the League Cup competition has provided many dramatic moments over the years.'

Open Goal

1. Which team played in the League Cup Final in three out of the four years from 1989 to 1992?

2. Who scored twelve goals for Spurs in the 1986-87 League Cup competition?

3. Which famous football pools company sponsored the tournament between 1986 and 1990?

4. Andy Gray scored the only goal of the 1980 League Cup Final. Which team was he playing with at that time?

5. Which manager steered Sheffield Wednesday to Rumbelows Cup success in 1991?

6. Who hit Manchester United's winner in the 1992 Final?

Half-Chance

7. Liverpool reached the League Cup Final six times between 1978 and 1987. Who played for them on every occasion?

8. The Anfield side were sensationally knocked out of the 1992 Rumbelows Cup by which Third Division team?

9. Can you name the American international who won a Rumbelows Cup medal in 1991?

10. Which ground staged League Cup Final replays in 1977 and 1978?

11. Manchester United defeated which Second Division side in the 1992 semi- final?

12. What delayed the kick-off of the second leg of the other 1992 semi- final between Spurs and Nottingham Forest?

Long-Range Shot

13. Which former Football League secretary is credited with originating the League Cup tournament?

14. Which Fourth Division team reached the Final in 1962?

15. Who was Chelsea manager when the Blues won the League Cup in 1965?

16. Can you name the two players who scored hat-tricks in Coventry's 5-4 win over Nottingham Forest in the 1990-91 Rumbelows Cup fourth round?

17. Bertie Auld, a European Cup winner with Celtic in 1967, had earlier won a Football League Cup medal with which club?

18. Which World Cup referee took charge of the 1992 Rumbelows Final?

Sharp in the Box

Between 1961 and 1992, five non-First Division clubs lifted the Football League Cup. Can you name them?

QUIZ 7
IN A DIFFERENT LEAGUE

'The cup successes of so many non-League sides just goes to show that there's a real depth of talent in the English game.'

Open Goal

1. Who were the 1992 GM Vauxhall Conference Champions?
2. Can you name the former Nottingham Forest, Norwich and Northern Ireland star who managed runners-up Wycombe Wanderers?
3. This famous old club dropped out the Football League in February 1962 but can nowadays be found playing in the HFS Loans League. Who are they?
4. Which Italian sportswear company took over sponsorship of the Isthmian League in 1991?
5. Which is the only club to have won both the FA Cup and the FA Amateur Cup during the 20th century?
6. What is the non-League 'Double'?

Half-Chance

7. Which Southern League club narrowly lost to Italian side Atalanta in the first round of the 1987-88 European Cup Winners' Cup?
8. The all-time leading goalscorer in the Vauxhall Conference was a member of the Barnet team which won promotion to the Football League in 1991. Can you name him?
9. Which is the only Scottish club playing in English non-League football?

10. In February 1978, 42,157 fans packed Newcastle's St James' Park to watch which Northern League side take on Third Division Wrexham in an FA Cup fifth round replay?

11. Which clubs compete in the FA Vase competition?

12. They play at a ground called Bucks Head and were managed at one time by England's 1966 World Cup goalkeeper Gordon Banks. Can you name this Shropshire club?

Long-Range Shot

13. Which was the last non-League club to win the FA Cup?

14. At which London club did Cyrille Regis begin his career?

15. Which former secretary of the FA later became president of Kingstonian?

16. VS Rugby enjoyed a successful season in the 1991-92 Beazer Homes Premier Division. What does the prefix VS stand for?

17. Ross County were the 1992 Champions of which League?

18. Who were the last winners of the FA Amateur Cup in 1974?

Sharp in the Box

Five clubs have played in the Vauxhall Conference in every season since the league began in 1979. How many of them can you name?

QUIZ 8
OTHER TOURNAMENTS

'There seems to be more tournaments than ever nowadays. At least they give smaller clubs the chance of picking up honours.'

Open Goal

1. Which two teams traditionally compete for the FA Charity Shield?

2. Can you name the young Scottish midfielder who hit two goals for Nottingham Forest in the 1992 Zenith Data Systems Cup Final?

3. At which famous rugby union ground was the 1992 Welsh Cup Final held?

4. The 1991 Italian League Champions thrashed West Ham 6-1 in the semi-finals of that year's Makita pre-season tournament at Highbury. Who were they?

5. Which Third Division team defeated Stockport County 1-0 in the Wembley Final of the Autoglass Trophy in May 1992?

6. What usually happens if the Charity Shield match finishes level after 90 minutes of play?

Half-Chance

7. What became England's first commercially sponsored tournament in 1971?

8. And what was the criterion for entry into that competition?

9. Who scored Everton's winning goal in the 1987 Charity Shield match, 15 years after his brother Allan had headed the only goal of the FA Cup Final?

10. Who were the 1992 Welsh Cup winners?

11. Which team set a record score for a Wembley Charity Shield victory in 1978?

12. Can you name either of the strikers who each scored hat-tricks in the 1989 Simod Cup Final between Everton and Nottingham Forest?

Long-Range Shot

13. In 1981, Scottish clubs ended their involvement in the Anglo-Scottish Cup tournament. What was ironic about the reason they gave for their withdrawal?

14. Which two teams drew 6-6 in a ZDS Cup first round tie in October 1991?

15. What was the Debenhams Cup?

16. Which goalkeeper scored in the 1967 Charity Shield match?

17. Who were the first and only winners of the Scottish Spring Cup in 1976?

18. In May 1988, over 80,000 fans watched which two Fourth Division sides meet at Wembley in the Sherpa Van Trophy Final?

Sharp in the Box

Can you name the five clubs which have won the Full Members/ZDS Cup under its various guises since 1986?

QUIZ 9
COME ON YOU SPURS

*'I had no hesitation when Tottenham came in for me in 1989.
They're one of the world's most famous clubs and they play the
sort of football I like.'*

1. Which European tournament have Spurs won twice?

2. Name the Argentinian World Cup stars who joined the club
in 1978.

3. This young defender, who shares a name with the capital
city of Scotland, made his debut for Spurs in 1990. Who is he?

4. Which bird is featured on Spurs' club crest?

5. Who skippered Tottenham to their FA Cup triumphs of
1981 and 1982?

6. Which Portuguese side did they defeat in the second round
of the 1991-92 European Cup Winners' Cup?

Half-Chance

7. From which fellow London club was midfielder Andy
Gray signed?

8. In the 1960s, what slight change did Spurs traditionally
make to their playing kit in European matches?

9. Who rammed home a free kick to give Tottenham a fifth
minute lead in the 1991 FA Cup semi-final against Arsenal at
Wembley?

10. Which England manager won a League Championship
medal with Spurs in 1951?

11. Which team ended Spurs' reign as FA Cup holders by
defeating them in the third round of the 1992 competition?

12. Who skippered the 'Double' team of 1960-61?

Long-Range Shot

13. When did Tottenham last play in the Second Division?

14. Can you name the young goalkeeper who appeared in several matches for Spurs during 1991-92, including two Cup Winners' Cup ties?

15. Who did Spurs play in the Charity Shield match, the season following their 'Double' victory?

16. Against which team did Spurs enjoy their record European victory, in 1971?

17. Who was the manager of the famous 'push and run' side of the late 1940s and early '50s?

18. In which position did Spurs finish in the 1991-92 First Division table?

Sharp in the Box

Three members of the Tottenham team which won the FA Cup in 1991 had played in the Final with other clubs – can you name them?

QUIZ 10
MY STRIKING PARTNERS

'Throughout my career, I've been fortunate enough to play alongside some of the best attackers in the game. Each has his own special qualities.'

Open Goal

1. Which Welsh international striker played alongside Gary at Barcelona?

2. From which fellow London club did Spurs sign Gordon Durie in 1991?

3. Which of Gary's former Leicester team-mates was the First Division's top League goalscorer in the 1988-89 and 1990-91 seasons?

4. For which country did one-time Everton colleague Graeme Sharp win twelve international caps?

5. Which of Gary's England partners has scored over 150 League goals for Wolves?

6. And which of them played at one time for Canadian side Vancouver Whitecaps?

Half-Chance

7. Who notched a double against both West Germany and the USA during England's summer tour of 1985?

8. Graeme Sharp wore the No.9 jersey for which team in the 1991-92 First Division?

9. What is Gordon Durie's nickname?

10. Can you name the Portuguese international who starred

alongside Gary for the Rest of the World side in the Football League Centenary match staged at Wembley in August 1987?

11. For which *Bundesliga* club did Mark Hughes play during his spell in European soccer?

12. How many goals did Alan Smith score in the home leg of Arsenal's 1991-92 European Cup tie against Austria Vienna?

Long-Range Shot

13. In which year did Peter Beardsley make his England debut?

14. Can you name the former Partick Thistle striker who scored 21 League goals for Leicester between 1980 and 1982?

15. Everton's Adrian Heath later followed Gary to Spanish football. For which team did he play?

16. Can you name the tall, gangling striker who opened the scoring for Barcelona in the 1989 European Cup-Winners' Cup Final?

17. Which of Gary's striking partners took part in the Scottish Skol Cup Final in 1985?

18. In 1982, Alan Smith won three semi-professional caps for England. Which non-League club was he with at that time?

Sharp in the Box

Between 1979 and 1992, Peter Beardsley was on the books of five English clubs. Can you name them?

QUIZ 11
SOCCER IN THE MIDLANDS

'Being from the Midlands, I like to see the area's teams do well – especially Leicester, my home town club.'

Open Goal

1. Which was the last Midlands club to win the League Championship?
2. Where do Nottingham Forest play their home matches?
3. Which club sold Dean Saunders and Mark Wright to Liverpool in the summer of 1991?
4. Can you name the manager who led Birmingham City to promotion from the Third Division during 1991-92?
5. In what colour of shirts do Leicester play?
6. Which of the Midlands clubs has played in the top English division since 1967?

Half-Chance

7. Which team has won more often in Aston Villa v Birmingham derby matches?
8. Who captained Wolves to three League Championships during the 1950s?
9. Which is the oldest club in the Midlands and possibly the world?
10. Which Aston Villa defender scored in both legs of their 1990-91 UEFA Cup victory over Czech side Banik Ostrava?
11. Can you name the Uruguayan team which defeated Nottingham Forest in the World Club Championship match of 1980?

12. Which Irish international striker played in Football League Cup Finals for both Leicester and Wolves?

Long-Range Shot

13. Who was Birmingham's top scorer in all competitions during 1991-92?

14. Which Midlands club did Ian Greaves manage between 1983 and 1989?

15. In both the 1969-70 and 1970-71 seasons, the First Division's leading goalscorer was a West Bromwich Albion player. Can you name the two strikers concerned?

16. Which Midlands team are nicknamed 'The Saddlers'?

17. Who is Leicester's most-capped player?

18. For which country did Notts County's Rachid Harkouk appear in the 1986 World Cup?

Sharp in the Box

Can you list the four men who have won the PFA Player of the Year award while on the books of a Midlands club?

QUIZ 12
THE CAPTAINS

'I was absolutely delighted when Graham Taylor made me captain of England. It was a tremendous honour to lead the lads out of the tunnel at Wembley.'

Open Goal

1. Which country did Ruud Gullit skipper in the 1992 European Championship?

2. Who is the Nottingham Forest captain who missed the club's 1992 Rumbelows Cup Final appearance?

3. Which team does Richard Gough lead?

4. Who captained England's World Cup winning side of 1966?

5. Which star midfielder was dubbed 'Captain Marvel' by Manchester United and England fans?

6. Who was the last goalkeeper to skipper a World Cup winning team?

Half-Chance

7. Which team did Julian Dicks captain in the 1991-92 English First Division?

8. Who was the QPR player who led England on eight occasions during the 1970s?

9. Who was the first British club captain to lift the European Cup?

10. Which one-time Wolves skipper later became a player-manager of Rotherham United and a director of Hull City?

11. Martin Buchan is the only man to have captained both Scottish and English FA Cup winning sides. Which two teams did he lead?

12. Who has twice skippered Arsenal to the League Championship in recent seasons?

Long-Range Shot

13. What age was Barry Venison when he captained Sunderland in the 1985 Milk Cup Final?

14. Who was the first Liverpool captain to lift the FA Cup?

15. Who is the only man to have been ordered off while captaining England?

16. Which club has supplied post-war captains to all four home countries?

17. What was the full christian name of famous Sunderland skipper Raich Carter?

18. What distinction does Cuthbert Ottaway hold?

Sharp in the Box

Name the four players called 'Bill' or 'Billy' who have captained post-war FA Cup winning teams.

QUIZ 13
THE PRIDE OF MERSEYSIDE

'Having played there with Everton, I know all about the passion that Merseyside fans have for the game.'

Open Goal

1. Name the player-manager who led Liverpool to the League and Cup Double in 1986.

2. What is Everton's rather sweet nickname?

3. Which Merseyside club plays at Prenton Park, Birkenhead?

4. Can you name the full-back who played in eight Championship-winning Liverpool teams between 1975 and 1985?

5. Which is the older club – Liverpool or Everton?

6. Which of the old city rivals has won the more derby encounters in the League?

Half-Chance

7. Which Everton defender scored his first goal for England in the 2-2 draw against Czechoslovakia in Prague in March 1992?

8. Who was the Hungarian international signed by Liverpool boss Graeme Souness during 1991-92?

9. Which London team knocked Everton out of the 1992 FA Cup?

10. This former Everton wing half masterminded Tranmere's progression from Division Four to Division Two between 1987 and 1991. What's his name?

11. Which two continental sides have Liverpool twice beaten in European tournament finals?

12. During the 1970s, which striker played and scored for both clubs in Merseyside derby matches?

Long-Range Shot

13. Who was the only Liverpool player to appear in all 51 League and cup matches during The Reds' successful 1987-88 season?

14. Which graduate of the GM Vauxhall national football school made his debut for Everton against Wimbledon in February 1989?

15. Who made his Scotland debut as a Liverpool player in 1979 but never actually played a first-team match at Anfield?

16. Name the Merseyside rivals who were team-mates in England's World Cup winning team of 1966.

17. Which team did Everton defeat in the 1989 FA Cup semi-final?

18. The first-ever orderings off in a Merseyside derby match occurred in the Anfield clash of October 1979. Can you name either of the players involved?

Sharp in the Box

Name the five men who managed Everton between 1970 and 1992.

QUIZ 14
IRISH CREAM

'Although the Republic's team has only recently made an impact in international soccer, Irish stars have always played a big part in English League football.'

Open Goal

1. Veteran Irish defender David O'Leary holds the appearance record at which London club?

2. Who was the last Irishman to finish as the English First Division's leading goalscorer?

3. For which two clubs did Frank Stapleton score FA Cup Final goals?

4. Which Irish star headed the extra-time goal against Spurs which took Nottingham Forest into the 1992 Rumbelows Cup Final?

5. Who was the striker who scored for Sunderland in every round of the 1992 FA Cup prior to the Final?

6. Which club bought Steve Staunton from Liverpool in 1991?

Half-Chance

7. Republic of Ireland striker Bernie Slaven was actually born in which country?

8. Which Irishman netted the only goal of the 1991 Rumbelows Cup Final?

9. What was Liam Brady's last English League club?

10. Can you name the London-born QPR and Arsenal defender who won five caps for the Republic during the 1970s?

11. Which of Ireland's 1990 World Cup team became player-manager of Millwall in 1992?

12. Which Midlands club did Johnny Giles boss from 1975 to 1977 and from 1984 to 1985?

Long-Range Shot

13. Can you name the three clubs for which Ray Houghton played before joining Liverpool in 1987?

14. In which year did Andy Townsend make his international debut?

15. Who was the Republic's first black international star?

16. Other than Ireland, midfielder Kevin Sheedy could have chosen to play for which country?

17. Irish wing star of the 1980s, Tony Galvin, has a degree in which European language?

18. Can you name the Arsenal player who was capped by Ireland at both soccer and rugby during the 1940s?

Sharp in the Box

Name the six other countries in the Republic of Ireland's qualifying group for the 1994 World Cup.

QUIZ 15
THE MEN WHO KEEP THEM OUT

'For 90 minutes, they're the arch-enemy of any striker, but I've got great respect for most goalkeepers.'

Open Goal

1. Leeds' John Lukic has won a Championship medal with which other club?

2. Who is the world's most-capped goalkeeper?

3. Can you name the Welsh international who kept goal for Sunderland in the 1992 FA Cup Final?

4. Which leading goalkeeper was dubbed 'Jungle Man' by his team-mates at Liverpool?

5. What nationality is Manchester United No.1 Peter Schmeichel?

6. With which two clubs did Ray Clemence gain FA Cup winners medals?

Half-Chance

7. In February 1992, former Scotland World Cup goalkeeper Jim Leighton returned to his home country to play for which team?

8. Who was the on-loan 'keeper who took Leighton's place in Manchester United's 1990 FA Cup Final team?

9. For which country did extrovert goalie Rene Higuita star in the 1990 World Cup finals?

10. Who played in the League Cup Finals of 1985 and 1991, for

Sunderland and Sheffield Wednesday respectively?

11. During 1991-92, Peter Shilton left Derby County to become player-manager of which Second Division club?

12. What was the Scottish connection between the respective goalkeepers in the Republic of Ireland v England match of November 1990?

Long-Range Shot

13. Can you name the three goalkeepers who appeared in the 1982 European Cup Final between Aston Villa and Bayern Munich?

14. What age was Derek Forster when he kept goal for Sunderland against Leicester in a 1964 First Division match?

15. Gareth Howells played in midfield for Spurs during 1991-92 but his goalkeeping brother David was unable to prevent which club being relegated from Division Three?

16. Can you name Motherwell's 1991 Scottish Cup Final hero who never played again for the club after falling out with manager Tommy McLean?

17. Why did Manchester United 'keeper Ray Wood spend much of the 1957 FA Cup Final playing on the right wing?

18. What unusual aid did both Jack Kelsey and Gordon Banks use in their goalkeeping?

Sharp in the Box

Name the four English clubs for which Chris Woods has played.

OH GARY, GARY ...

'I've quite a few footballing namesakes. See how much you know about them ...'

Open Goal

1. Which Gary moved from Liverpool to Celtic in August 1991?

2. Rangers and England full-back Gary Stevens played in three FA Cup Finals for which club during the 1980s?

3. Which Manchester United defender was capped by England as a Second Division player in 1988?

4. Do you know which Gary scored 18 League goals for Aston Villa's Championship side of 1981?

5. Can you name either of the clubs for which Gary McAllister played before joining Leeds United?

6. Who moved from Nottingham Forest to Manchester United for £1.25 million in October 1980?

Half-Chance

7. Steve Bull's cousin Gary notched 22 goals for which club in the 1991-92 Fourth Division?

8. Can you name Manchester United's 1985 Cup Final goalkeeper who was forced to quit top class football by a bad knee injury?

9. Who was the Welsh midfielder who starred for Leeds 1991-92 Championship team?

10. Which Gary swopped the red of Liverpool for the blue of

Everton during 1991-92?

11. If you saw Gary McGinnis tackle Gary Mackay during 1991-92, which two Scottish Premier League teams would you have been watching?

12. Who was the subject of a £1 million deal between Watford and Aston Villa in March 1991?

Long-Range Shot

13. Which team did Gary Gillespie captain at the age of 17?

14. Can you name the Republic of Ireland 'B' international goalkeeper who joined Bury from Newcastle in 1989?

15. Gary Owers, who played for Sunderland in the 1992 FA Cup Final, is married to which British ice-skating champion?

16. At which club did Gary Bowyer play alongside his dad Ian in April 1990?

17. Who was Spurs' substitute in both the 1981 and 1982 FA Cup Finals?

18. Sunderland's Gary Bennett was ordered off along with which Coventry City player after a hot-tempered clash in a Littlewoods Cup tie of January 1990?

Sharp in the Box

The Nottingham Forest side beaten by Spurs in the 1991 FA Cup Final contained three players with the christian name Gary. Can you name them?

QUIZ 17
SWEDEN '92 EUROPEAN CHAMPIONSHIP

'Denmark's victory in Euro'92 was a real surprise to everyone. It just underlined how unpredictable football can be.'

Open Goal

1. Which country did the Danes defeat in the Final?

2. Which of the tournament favourites lost on a penalty shoot-out in the semis?

3. Can you name the Swedish marksman who hit three goals in the competition, including the strike which knocked England out?

4. Which city staged the Final?

5. Who netted England's only goal?

6. Which country was expelled from the tournament only eight days before it began?

Half-Chance

7. Which Scotland player scored his first goal in 26 internationals when he was on target in the match against the CIS?

8. How many of their five matches did Denmark actually win?

9. Who was the German captain who broke his arm in his team's opening game?

10. Where did England play their first two matches?

41

11. Which Scotland player was appearing in the country of his birth?

12. Which national manager complained that his team had only played well for a total of 25 minutes during their three matches?

Long-Range Shot

13. Who played in the right-back position for England against Sweden?

14. How many Rangers players took part in the Scotland-CIS match?

15. Can you name the manager of the triumphant Denmark team?

16. What unusual basis did Scotland use for the numbering of their players?

17. Who was Germany's top scorer in the final tournament, with three goals?

18. What nationality was the Final referee Bruno Galler?

Sharp in the Box

Only two of the competing teams in Euro'92 didn't contain any English-based players. Who were they?

QUIZ 18
WORLD CUP '86

'After a bad start, England really came good in Mexico. We were disappointed not to progress further than the quarter-finals.'

Open Goal

1. Who scored a goal with 'the Hand of God'?
2. Can you name the giant stadium in Mexico City which staged the Final between Argentina and West Germany?
3. England notched their first win of the tournament against which country?
4. Which goalkeeper won a world-record 119th cap during the finals?
5. Two players in the England squad shared the same name. Who were they?
6. Who scored Scotland's only goal?

Half-Chance

7. Can you name the two England players who were with a foreign club at that time?
8. The World Cup holders met the European Champions in a second round match. Which teams were involved and who won?
9. Against which country was Ray Wilkins given his marching orders?
10. Nico Claesen, who scored three goals for Belgium, joined which English club later that year?

11. Who kept goal for West Germany in the Final?

12. What was the injury which forced Bryan Robson to bow out of the tournament?

Long-Range Shot

13. Which country notched the biggest win of the 1986 finals?

14. In the quarter-finals, France defeated Brazil in a penalty shoot-out. Why should the referee not have allowed Bellone's penalty for France to stand?

15. What was the name of the official mascot – a smiling, green chilli pepper?

16. For which country did 'Romerito' net two first round goals?

17. What dramatic name did the locals give to Scotland's tough first round group?

18. Who was the only English referee to officiate in the finals?

Sharp in the Box

Seven Manchester United players travelled to Mexico as members of four World Cup squads. Can you name them?

QUIZ 19
ENGLAND'S LIONS

'It's a highly illustrious list of names that have worn the famous white shirt of England down the years.'

Open Goal

1. Can you name either of the two Arsenal strikers in England's 1992 European Championship squad?

2. Which 23-year-old Spurs midfielder really established himself on the international scene during the 1990 World Cup?

3. Who were the last pair of brothers to play together for England?

4. Which England star is the son of a former Jamaican international?

5. In what way was Steve Bull different from the rest of the 1990 World Cup squad?

6. Three players appeared for England in each of the 1982, 1986 and 1990 World Cups. Can you name any two of the three?

Half-Chance

7. Who scored his first international goal for six years during England's friendly against the CIS in Moscow in April 1992?

8. What is the nickname of the 84-times-capped Ray Wilkins?

9. Which member of England's 1966 World Cup winning team played in contact lenses?

10. Can you name the Southampton forward who was

45

England's top goalscorer in the 1973-74, '75-76 and '76-77 seasons?

11. Striker Malcolm Macdonald netted five goals against Cyprus in 1975. How many of them were headers?

12. At the end of the 1991-92 season, who held the record for being the most-substituted England player of all time?

Long-Range Shot

13. How many caps did midfielder Glenn Hoddle win – 43, 53 or 63?

14. Which club provided seven players for the England team which played against Italy in 1934?

15. Can you name the South African-born, Ipswich Town midfield man who was capped twice by England in the 1975 Home International championship?

16. Which England wing star of the 1940s and '50s was nicknamed 'The Preston Plumber'?

17. With which two clubs was Rodney Marsh capped?

18. Who scored for both sides in England's friendly against Holland in March 1988?

Sharp in the Box

Who were the two Leeds United players in England's squad for the 1992 European Championship in Sweden?

'I think we proved a lot of people wrong when we reached the semi-finals in Italy. With a bit of luck, we could've gone all the way.'

Open Goal

1. Who was the manager of 1990 World Cup winners West Germany?

2. Which country defeated England in the third place play-off match?

3. Can you name the two players sent off in the West Germany v Holland second round game in Milan?

4. Which defender headed England's winner in their group match with Egypt?

5. Scotland crashed to a shock defeat in their opening match. Which Central American side beat them 1-0?

6. Who was the German full-back who notched three goals in the tournament – including the winner in the Final?

Half-Chance

7. Italy's Roberto Baggio scored what was probably the best individual goal of the 1990 finals against which team?

8. Which Argentinian striking star missed the Final through suspension?

9. Which country had two players ordered off in the tournament's opening match?

10. Which England forward had a goal disallowed in the first

half of the second round meeting with Belgium?

11. Where was the England-West Germany semi-final played?

12. In the Final, which German striker was brought down in the penalty area, gaining the spot kick award which decided the match?

Long-Range Shot

13. Which player committed more fouls than any other in Italia '90?

14. Who notched his first-ever international goal in Scotland's 2-1 victory over Sweden in Genoa?

15. Which team had the leakiest defence in the tournament, conceding 11 goals in total?

16. Can you name the Argentinian goalkeeper who broke his leg in the match against the USSR?

17. Which team finished bottom of England's first round group?

18. Name the Real Madrid midfielder who hit four goals in Spain's four matches.

Sharp in the Box

Can you name the four beaten quarter-finalists in Italia '90?

EUROPEAN CHAMPIONSHIP '88

'This tournament was something of a disaster for England. We just didn't perform at all.'

Open Goal

1. Which of the teams in the 1988 European Chapionship was playing in the final stages of a major tournament for the first time?
2. Who was the Dutchman who netted a hat-trick against England?
3. Which Italian club had he joined the previous season?
4. Where was the Final played?
5. Who was the Liverpool midfielder who headed the only goal of the Ireland v England first round match?
6. Can you name the two brothers who helped Holland to victory?

Half-Chance

7. Which of the finalists was managed by Sepp Piontek?
8. Who was the striker, then with Sampdoria, who scored the only goal of the Italy v Spain group match?
9. Which Scottish club supplied three members of the Republic of Ireland team?
10. Who was the 1986 European Footballer of the Year who missed a penalty in the Final?
11. Which 37-year-old former Manchester United and

Ipswich star played in the triumphant Dutch side?

12. Who was the Arsenal full-back who won the last of his 86 caps in England's match against the USSR?

Long-Range Shot

13. Which country were the top scorers in the qualifying competition for the 1988 European Championship?

14. Why did the Soviet Union play in white in their group match against Ireland?

15. Who was the French official who refereed the Final?

16. What was similar about both of Italy's goalscorers against Denmark?

17. Which country's 1-0 win in Bulgaria allowed Ireland to qualify for the finals?

18. Which club side provided the basis of the Soviet Union's team in 1988?

Sharp in the Box

Can you name the seven German cities, other than Munich, which staged matches in the 1988 European Championship?

QUIZ 22
WORLD CUP QUALIFYING

'With the rewards so great for making the finals, there's an awful lot at stake in World Cup qualifying matches now.'

Open Goal

1. Against which Scandinavian country did England begin their qualifying campaign for the 1994 World Cup?
2. Which three-times World Cup winners are competing in Scotland's '94 qualifying group?
3. Can you name the two countries which are exempt from the current qualifying competition?
4. Which national team has, for political reasons, played in both European and Australasian qualifying groups?
5. Who was the Scotland manager who died tragically at the end of the World Cup qualifier against Wales in 1985?
6. Which country topped England's qualifying group for the 1990 tournament?

Half-Chance

7. Can you name the Aston Villa winger who missed out on the 1990 World Cup finals after his Trinidad and Tobago side lost narrowly to the USA in a final qualifying round match of November 1989?
8. Which two countries went to war after a World Cup qualifying match in 1969?
9. When did England last fail to make the finals?
10. Against which country did Wales' Mark Hughes score

with a spectacular high volley in a 1985 match at Wrexham?

11. Which was the only country not to concede a goal in the entire 1990 World Cup qualifying competition?

12. Who scored in five successive qualifiers for Scotland between 1988 and 1989?

Long-Range Shot

13. Which country did England meet for the first time during the qualifying rounds of the 1990 World Cup?

14. Which team scored the first goal of the current World Cup tournament?

15. Can you name the Polish goalkeeper who helped eliminate England in 1973 with a string of miraculous saves?

16. Which country trounced Fiji 13-0 in a 1981 World Cup qualifying match?

17. Who netted Northern Ireland's first goal of their 1994 campaign in the 2-2 draw against Lithuania in April 1992?

18. Which European country refused to play a 1973 World Cup eliminator in Chile because the Santiago stadium had been used for the execution of political prisoners?

Sharp in the Box

Can you name the five other nations in Wales' 1994 World Cup qualifying group?

BEST OF BRITISH

'For countries so small, the Scots, Welsh and Northern Irish have an impressive record in international competition.'

Open Goal

1. In which year's World Cup finals did Northern Ireland win a famous victory over hosts Spain?

2. Who was the Manchester United winger who became the youngest Welsh cap of all time when he played against Germany in October 1991?

3. What colour of jerseys do Scotland play in?

4. Name the manager who guided Northern Ireland to two World Cup final tournaments during the 1980s.

5. Who netted Wales' winning goal against world champions Germany in Cardiff in June 1991?

6. In which year did all four home nations reach the World Cup finals?

Half-Chance

7. Scotland's Under-21 side lost narrowly in the semi-finals of the 1992 European Championship. Which country defeated them 1-0 on aggregate?

8. Dean Saunders' goal gave Wales their first-ever victory over which former World Cup winners in September 1991?

9. Can you name the 59-times-capped Northern Ireland international who has managed both Arsenal and Tottenham?

10. In which year's World Cup finals did Scotland remain undefeated in their three matches?

11. Who won a record 73rd cap for Wales in the 1991 European Championship match against Luxembourg?

12. In September 1991, whose hat-trick against the Faroe Islands saw him equal the Northern Ireland goalscoring record?

Long-Range Shot

13. At which club was Dean Saunders first capped?

14. Who was Scotland's manager at the 1978 World Cup in Argentina?

15. Wales have only once progressed beyond the first round of the European Championship; in which year did they do that?

16. How many Northern Ireland caps did George Best win?

17. Who was the last player to score four goals in one match for Scotland?

18. In November 1983, Northern Ireland became the first team to win a European Championship match on West German soil. Who scored their winning goal in Hamburg?

Sharp in the Box

Can you name the three men who preceded Terry Yorath as Wales' team manager?

QUIZ 24
WORLD CUP PAST HISTORY

'Every World Cup tournament has its own particular memories for fans – famous goals, famous saves and even famous tears!.'

Open Goal

1. Can you name the only South American country to have won a World Cup tournament which was held in Europe?

2. Which was the last host nation to win the cup?

3. Who was the Italian striker who top scored in the 1982 World Cup in Spain?

4. Which team did England defeat in the semi-finals in 1966?

5. Can you name the Dutch superstar who refused to travel to the 1978 World Cup, much to the disappointment of his country's fans?

6. What was the result of every opening match in the World Cup tournaments between 1966 and 1978 inclusive?

Half-Chance

7. Who skippered Brazil to victory in 1970?

8. Which was the first World Cup tournament to feature 24 teams?

9. Who missed England's final three matches in 1966 after sustaining a 4" shin gash in the group match against France?

10. The player who scored the first goal of the 1974 World Cup finals also scored the last goal of the 1982 tournament. Who was he?

11. Which was the lowest-scoring World Cup tournament in terms of goals per game?

12. Who was the first player to score in every round?

Long-Range Shot

13. In which year did the USA shock England with a 1-0 victory?

14. Which competing country had the biggest travelling support in the 1974 World Cup in West Germany?

15. Who was the Dutchman who wore a plaster cast on his injured arm during the 1978 Final against Argentina?

16. In which year were substitutes first allowed in the tournament?

17. Can you name the two countries who, in 1958, played out the first ever 0-0 draw in the World Cup finals?

18. What was the name of England's 1982 mascot?

Sharp in the Box

Name the six European countries which have lost in a World Cup Final.

QUIZ 25
THE MANAGERS

'I've had several managers throughout my career and I think I can safely say that I've learned something from all of them.'

Open Goal

1. Who replaced Bobby Gould as West Bromwich Albion manager in May 1992?

2. Which team has Joe Royle bossed since 1982?

3. The Bald Eagle led Portsmouth to the 1992 FA Cup semi-finals. Who is he?

4. Which team did Brian Clough guide to League Championship success in 1972?

5. Who was the 1992 Manager of the Year in England?

6. Can you name the caretaker boss who took Sunderland to the 1992 FA Cup Final before being confirmed as club manager?

Half-Chance

7. Which leading manager is nicknamed 'Harry'?

8. At which club did Trevor Francis begin his management career?

9. Glaswegian Jimmy Sirrel had three spells in charge of which East Midlands club between 1969 and 1987?

10. What is Lou Macari's full first name?

11. Which former Liverpool star led Bolton to victory in the 1989 Sherpa Van Trophy Final?

12. Which Football League manager reached the top of the

German pop charts in 1979?

Long-Range Shot

13. Who managed the Great Britain team in the 1948 Olympic Games football tournament?

14. Who was the first manager to take Brighton into the First Division?

15. Who was the youngest boss in the 1991-92 Football League?

16. Can you name the ex-Celtic midfielder who was appointed manager of Scottish First Division side Kilmarnock in 1992?

17. Who preceded Jack Charlton as Republic of Ireland boss?

18. In 1966, Ted Bates led which club into Division One for the first time in their history?

Sharp in the Box

Can you name the three clubs which Graham Taylor bossed before becoming England manager?

QUIZ 26
HAVE BOOTS WILL TRAVEL

'In football, it's important to make the right move at the right time.'

Open Goal

1. Ray Wilkins has been on the books of football clubs in four different countries. At which club did he begin his illustrious career?

2. Can you name the striker who moved from Sunderland to Crystal Palace and then on to Derby during 1991-92?

3. West Ham became this goalscorer's sixth London club when he signed for them in March 1992. Who is he?

4. Who became Britain's first £2 million player when he moved from Newcastle to Spurs in 1988?

5. Veteran defender John McClelland has played League football in all four home countries since 1974. For which country has he played internationally?

6. Which member of England's 1966 World Cup team made over 100 League appearances for each of Blackpool, Everton, Arsenal and Southampton?

Half-Chance

7. During his career, this full-back was on the books of all four of the big North-Western clubs – Liverpool, Everton, Manchester United and City. He also won one England cap in 1977. Who is he?

8. From which club did Spurs sign Jason Cundy?

9. Can you recognize this player by his transfer trail: Nottingham Forest – Aston Villa – Spurs – Nottingham Forest – Leeds?

10. During 1991-92, Clyde had in their ranks a far-travelled striker, with a European Cup runners-up medal from 1986. Can you name him?

11. Charlie George helped Arsenal win the 'Double' in 1971, but at which club did he win his only England cap?

12. Can you name the two clubs for which Steve Bruce played before joining Manchester United?

Long-Range Shot

13. At which club did Graeme Souness begin his professional career?

14. Who, in September 1979, became the first uncapped player to be sold for more than £1 million?

15. For how many different Football League clubs did Leslie Roberts play between 1921 and 1936?

16. Colourful England striker Frank Worthington was a man of many clubs but at which of them did he win a Second Division Championship medal in 1970?

17. Who played in the European Cup competition for three different Scottish clubs?

18. What is the maximum period for which a club may take a player on loan in the Football League?

Sharp in the Box

Can you name the four clubs withwhich centre-half Dave Watson won 65 England caps between 1974 and 1982?

QUIZ 27
THE FOREIGN LEGION

'English fans seem to enjoy watching the foreign stars. They add a certain je ne sais quoi!'

Open Goal

1. Which Frenchman helped Leeds win the League Championship in 1992?

2. Who was the 'Great Dane' in Liverpool's 1992 FA Cup winning side?

3. Which team did Manchester United's Andrei Kanchelskis play for in the 1992 European Championship?

4. Can you name the Brazilian who joined Newcastle in 1987?

5. During 1991-92, which two London First Division clubs had Czechoslovakian goalkeepers?

6. Who was the Swedish international defender who played for the Football League select against the Italian League in 1991?

Half-Chance

7. Who was the last continental player to score in the FA Cup Final?

8. From which club did Arsenal sign Anders Limpar?

9. Which Sheffield Wednesday defender played against Scotland in the 1990 World Cup finals?

10. Which English club did Argentinian World Cup star Alberto Tarantini join in 1978?

11. Who was the German prisoner-of-war who won an FA

Cup winners medal with Manchester City in 1956, despite breaking his neck during the Final?

12. Who is the only overseas player to have been voted England's Footballer of the Year?

Long-Range Shot

13. Goalkeeper Pavel Srnicek, who joined Newcastle in January 1991, was formerly a soldier in which country's army?

14. Can you name the member of Zimbabwe's Olympic team who played in attack for Coventry during 1991-92?

15. Nestor Lorenzo, who joined Swindon in October 1990, had achieved what rather ignominious distinction three months previously?

16. Who was the Oxford United player who appeared for New Zealand against England in the summer of 1991?

17. Can you name the Dane who became the first overseas player to win a European competition medal with a British club, when he played for Newcastle in the 1969 Fairs Cup Final?

18. Who was the German, thought to have been the Football League's first foreign import in 1907?

Sharp in the Box

Two members of Liverpool's 1986 'Double' team were born in South Africa. Can you name them?

QUIZ 28
EARLY EXCHANGES

'The opening period of many games can be quite hectic as players seek to establish an advantage over their opponents.'

Open Goal

1. Who holds the record for England's fastest-ever goal in the World Cup finals?
2. Against which country did he score it in 1982?
3. During the 1970s, which team lost a World Cup Final despite taking the lead in the first minute?
4. Who was booked within five seconds of the kick-off in the 1992 FA Cup fifth round tie between Chelsea and Sheffield United?
5. Who headed Spurs into a second minute lead in the 1987 FA Cup Final?
6. Bradford's Jim Fryatt claimed a very quick goal in April 1965. How long after kick-off did he allegedly score?

Half-Chance

7. Who was the Manchester United and Ireland player ordered off after only 85 seconds of the First Division match at Southampton in January 1987?
8. Which Arsenal defender put through his own goal after 16 seconds of the Gunners' match at Sheffield Wednesday in February 1990?
9. Jackie Milburn was on the scoresheet within 45 seconds of the start of the 1955 FA Cup Final. For which team did he net?

10. Who scored Wembley's quickest-ever goal, for England against Yugoslavia in 1989?

11. Uruguay's Jose Batista received his marching orders in the first minute of a 1986 World Cup match in Mexico. Who were the opposition?

12. Which country notched the fastest goal of the 1990 World Cup after only four minutes of their Group D match against the United Arab Emirates in Bologna?

Long-Range Shot

13. Who was the on-loan player who hit Portsmouth's 90-second winning goal in the FA Cup sixth round tie with Nottingham Forest in March 1992?

14. How long was Bologna's Giuseppe Lorenzo on the pitch before he was red carded in the 1990 Italian League match with Parma?

15. In the 1973 European Cup Final between Ajax and Juventus, who headed the Dutchmen into a fourth-minute lead?

16. Derek Johnstone headed past Jim Cruickshank in the first minute of the 1976 Scottish Cup Final. Which teams were playing?

17. Which England forward was on target within 17 seconds during the 1947 match against Portugal in Lisbon?

18. Hungary trounced England 6-3 at Wembley in 1953. Can you name their deep-lying centre-forward who netted the first of his three goals in the very first minute of the game?

Sharp in the Box

Can you name the four teams which have come from behind to win a World Cup Final?

QUIZ 29
YOU ARE THE REF

'I've never really had many problems with referees. It helps to appreciate that they don't have an easy job.'

Open-Goal

1. Can a goal be scored directly from a corner-kick?
2. How many steps may a goalkeeper take after he has controlled the ball with his hands?
3. Can a penalty-taker score from a rebound?
4. How many yards should opposing players be from the ball at the taking of a free-kick?
5. Can a player ever be offside in his own half of the pitch?
6. What is the distance of the penalty-spot from the goal-line?

Half-Chance

7. True or false: the maximum amount of injury time that can be added on at the end of each half is ten minutes?
8. How does the referee signal a direct free-kick?
9. Can a linesman give a player offside?
10. Should a player be allowed to wear a wrist watch while playing?
11. True or false: all players, except the kicker and the goalkeeper, have to be behind the ball at a penalty kick?
12. What does a linesman indicate by holding his flag in a horizontal position above his head?

Long-Range Shot

13. What should be awarded if a defender inside the penalty-area pushes an opponent who is just outside it?

14. Is it permissable for the goalposts to be painted in black and white stripes?

15. Can a defender swop places with the regular goalkeeper at a penalty kick?

16. If a player shouts 'leave it' to a team mate, should the referee take any action?

17. What are the maximum dimensions of a pitch which is used for international matches?

18. Which is the only Law of the Game which has no International Board decisions applied to it?

Sharp in the Box

Four penalty offences can be committed with the hand. Can you name them?

QUIZ 30
4-3-3

'4-3-3, 4-4-2, 3-5-2 – soccer formations are almost a science in themselves now!'

Open Goal

1. Who wore the No. 4 shirt for England in the 1992 European Championship finals?

2. Which of the Bristol teams suffered three successive relegations between 1980 and 1982?

3. Which famous player appeared in three World Cup winning teams for Brazil?

4. Which country has been represented in each of the last four UEFA Cup Finals?

5. Can you name the three major trophies won by Liverpool in the 1983-84 season?

6. Three bothers turned out for Southampton against Sheffield Wednesday in October 1988. What was their surname?

Half-Chance

7. Name the Spanish striker who hit four World Cup goals against Denmark in 1986?

8. What are Edinburgh's three Scottish League clubs?

9. Can you name the three Manchester United players who have been European Footballer of the Year?

10. Four players were ordered off in a stormy Scottish Cup quarter-final tie in March 1991. Which teams were playing?

11. Which two countries drew all three of their first round matches in the 1982 World Cup?

12. Since 1970, three German teams have played in the European Cup Final. What are they?

Long-Range Shot

13. Which team defeated Derby County 4-3 away from home in the fourth round of the 1991-92 FA Cup?

14. Three players grabbed hat-tricks in Manchester City's 10-1 thrashing of Huddersfield in November 1987. Can you name them?

15. In which year did the Football League introduce three points for a win?

16. Egyptian international Hossam Hassan fired four UEFA Cup goals against Celtic in 1991. Which team was he on target for?

17. In which year did it take three matches to settle the outcome of the Football League Cup Final?

18. Who was the Real Madrid star of the 1950s and '60s who played at international level for three different countries?

Sharp in the Box

England were the first World Cup-winning team to use a 4-3-3 formation. How many of their 'back four' can you name?

DRAMATIC DEBUTS

'I'll always remember my first League appearance – for Leicester against Oldham on New Year's Day, 1979.'

Open Goal

1. Who was the striker, then with Southampton, who scored on his England debut against France in February 1992?

2. In September 1981, Trevor Francis made a scoring debut for which club, shortly after signing from Nottingham Forest?

3. Which international star was ordered off on his Scottish League debut in 1986?

4. Who scored debut goals for Chelsea, Spurs, West Ham and England?

5. Steve Bull scored on his first England appearance against which of the home countries in 1989?

6. True or false: in 1977, Celtic's Joe Craig scored for Scotland without having kicked a ball in international football?

Half-Chance

7. How many goals did Len Shackleton bag on his debut for Newcastle against Newport in October 1946?

8. Who scored the first of 30 international goals on his Scotland debut against Wales in Cardiff in 1958?

9. Against which team did Alan Shearer grab a hat-trick on his First Division debut?

10. In May 1984, who launched himself onto the international scene by netting Wales' winner against England in the last

Home Championship meeting between the countries?

11. Can you name the goalkeeper, later to play for Watford and Manchester City, who saved a penalty in the first minute of his Football League debut match, for Birmingham against Sunderland in 1980?

12. Against which country did Scotland's John Robertson score on his international debut in 1990?

Long-Range Shot

13. Where did Ian Wright mark his first appearance for Arsenal with a goal in a Rumbelows Cup tie?

14. How long did it take Barry Jones to score his first goal in Notts County's colours in March 1967?

15. Striker Bobby Davison scored on his Leeds debut in 1987. At which club had he been leading goalscorer in the previous four seasons?

16. Who was the West Ham striker who scored on his first and only appearance for England, against Iceland in 1982?

17. Against which team did David Platt score in his first Italian League game for Bari in September 1991?

18. Who was the last player to make a scoring debut for England in a World Cup finals match?

Sharp in the Box

On the opening day of the 1991-92 season, three players scored on their League debut for Aston Villa at Sheffield Wednesday. How many of them can you name?

QUIZ 32
SUPER SUBS

'I've not been on the bench very often but I did make my England debut as a sub for Tony Woodcock against Scotland in 1984.'

Open Goal

1. In which recent FA Cup Final were four of the five goals scored by substitutes?

2. Who netted twice for Liverpool in that match?

3. And who equalized twice for Everton?

4. Who was the veteran Cameroon substitute who came off the bench to hit four goals during the 1990 World Cup finals?

5. For which team did Ian Wright score two FA Cup Final goals as a substitute in 1990?

6. Which international superstar of the 1970s regularly wore the No. 14 jersey from the start of matches?

Half-Chance

7. Who netted four goals in five appearances as substitute for Manchester United during March and April 1990?

8. For which team was Ray Kennedy a scoring sub in the 1970 Fairs Cup Final first leg against Anderlecht?

9. In which year's World Cup Final did a substitute score a goal before being replaced himself?

10. Who was Liverpool's 'supersub' of the 1970s who later played for Lucerne, Wigan, Oldham, Beveren and Tranmere?

11. Eddie Kelly was the first No. 12 to score in an FA Cup Final,

71

but who originally claimed the goal which Kelly scored?

12. Which current Scottish manager sent his country to the 1974 World Cup finals by heading a decisive goal against Czechoslovakia after he had replaced Kenny Dalglish?

Long-Range Shot

13. Who was Spurs' matchwinning sub in the 1973 League Cup Final against Norwich?

14. Paul Gascoigne scored his first England goal as a substitute in the Wembley World Cup match against which country in April 1989?

15. Who was the first substitute to score in a World Cup Final?

16. Can you name the sub who headed Aberdeen's dramatic late winner in the 1983 European Cup-Winners' Cup Final?

17. In December 1982, both of England's substitutes against Luxembourg managed to get on the scoresheet. Who were they?

18. Lazlo Kiss came off the bench to grab a hat-trick in a 1982 World Cup finals match. For which country was he playing?

Sharp in the Box

During 1991-92, seven different players scored League goals for Leeds after coming on as a substitute. Who were they?

72

QUIZ 33
QUITE A SEASON – 1991-92

'It was exciting to watch another nail-biting climax to the Championship race with Leeds eventually just pipping Manchester United for the title.'

Open Goal

1. Which London team were the First Division's top scorers in 1991-92?

2. Where did England clinch their European Championship place in November?

3. Can you remember which Italian side knocked Liverpool out of the UEFA Cup?

4. Who played his 90th and last international match for England against Turkey in October?

5. Which club's chairman caused a storm with his comments about black players in a Channel Four documentary?

6. Which club's fans staged a series of pitch invasions to demonstrate against a proposed bond scheme?

Half-Chance

7. Who scored twice on his Scottish League debut for Rangers in November?

8. What was the result of Barnet's first-ever Football League match?

9. Who chipped Liverpool goalkeeper Mike Hooper from 45 yards during Arsenal's sensational 4-0 win over The Reds on Easter Monday?

10. Which West Midlands club were playing in the Third Division for the first time during 1991-92?

11. Who was the Celtic striker who scored on his international debut for the Republic of Ireland against Switzerland in March?

12. In September, Leeds notched their first League win over Liverpool for 18 years. Who scored the game's only goal?

Long-Range Shot

13. Can you name the QPR striker who silenced the Old Trafford crowd by scoring a hat-trick against Manchester United on New Year's Day?

14. Who replaced Nigel Martyn in goal after the Palace 'keeper had been sent off in a tempestuous derby with Wimbledon in August?

15. What were the results of the two First Division derby games between Sheffield Wednesday and Sheffield United?

16. Who was involved in an airport row with manager Andy Roxburgh as the Scotland party arrived home from their European Championship match in Switzerland?

17. Which team inflicted Leeds' heaviest defeat of the season in April?

18. Can you name the striker who scored a hat-trick against Nottingham Forest on the last day of the 1991-92 season, just three weeks after having been listed as a free transfer by his club?

Sharp in the Box

Name the three men who managed Wimbledon during the 1991-92 season.

QUIZ 34
ROUND THE GROUNDS

'I must have played in over 100 different football stadia. My favourite English League ground is Everton's Goodison Park.'

Open Goal

1. Where do Chelsea play?
2. Hillsborough is home to which club?
3. What is Scotland's national football stadium called?
4. This club has played home matches at Selhurst Park and Upton Park since leaving their own ground, The Valley, in 1985. Who are they?
5. Which stadium staged its first-ever FA Cup semi-final in April 1991?
6. True or false: Manchester United's Old Trafford ground is used for Test cricket during the summer months?

Half-Chance

7. Which Scottish League club's ground is in England?
8. Plough Lane is the former home of which English Premier League club?
9. Where do Ipswich Town play?
10. In which town is Grimsby's Blundell Park actually situated?
11. The 'North Bank' is the home supporters' end of which London ground?
12. On the opening day of the 1986-87 season, the Victoria

Ground, Hartlepool staged two Football League matches. Apart from the local side, who else played 'at home' that day and why?

Long-Range Shot

13. Which ground holds the record for the highest Fourth Division attendance and also for the lowest crowd ever recorded at a First Division match?

14. In 1938, British Prime Minister Chamberlain met Adolf Hitler at a place called Oberwiesenfeld. Which famous stadium is now situated on that site?

15. What have Ninian Park, Dean Court and McDiarmid Park in common?

16. Which club's pitch was voted the best in the First Division by the League Playing Surfaces Committee in 1991-92?

17. Who plays at Springfield Park?

18. At which ground is the John Ireland Stand situated 40 yards from the pitch?

Sharp in the Box

Three Scottish grounds share their name with the resident club. What are they?

QUITE A SEASON 1990-91

'This season ended perfectly for us at Spurs with the Cup Final victory over Nottingham Forest.'

Open Goal

1. In October 1990, 21 players were involved in a brawl during a match between which two First Division clubs?

2. Who quit Rangers to become Liverpool manager in April?

3. Which international superstar was found guilty of drugs charges in March?

4. Which former England centre-back became player-manager of Coventry City in November?

5. Who was the veteran Liverpool and Scotland defender who retired in March?

6. Mark Hateley's two goals clinched the Scottish League Championship for Rangers on the last day of the season. Which team took them all the way in the title race?

Half-Chance

7. In February, who was criticized in the Dutch press as being 'too soft' to manage PSV Eindhoven?

8. Which First Division club ended a long-standing ban on away fans in May 1991?

9. Which teams fought out an exciting 4-4 draw, in front of 38,000 fans, in an FA Cup fifth round replay?

10. Which country did England defeat 1-0 in their first match under Graham Taylor?

11. Who scored on his England debut against Turkey in May?

12. Can you remember which other two national sides competed in the England Challenge Cup?

Long-Range Shot

13. In February, Arsenal suffered their first defeat in 23 League matches. Which team beat them 2-1?

14. Who was the West Ham defender ordered off in the 1991 FA Cup semi-final against Nottingham Forest at Villa Park?

15. Which team became Manchester United's geographically-closest European competition opponents of all time?

16. Where did Liverpool win 7-1 in March?

17. Apart from losing the match, why did Spurs have a miserable trip to Chelsea in December?

18. Which two members of Southend's staff did Swiss club Zurich Grasshoppers want to sign in October?

Sharp in the Box

Name the clubs who finished in the top three places in the 1990-91 Third Division, thus winning their second consecutive promotion.

QUIZ 36
ON THE SPOT

'The penalty kick has been with us for over 100 years but, with so many cup ties being decided by shoot-outs these days, it's more important than ever.'

Open Goal

1. Which was the first team to win an FA Cup semi-final on a penalty shoot-out?

2. Where should a goalkeeper be at the taking of a penalty-kick?

3. Which was the last team to win the European Cup after a shoot-out?

4. Which TV pundit did John Aldridge blame for his penalty miss in Tranmere's 1991 Rumbelows Cup match against Halifax?

5. Which of the Manchester teams scored eight goals from penalties in the 1991-92 First Division season?

6. In which year's World Cup Final was a spot-kick awarded for the first time?

Half-Chance

7. Who was the Northern Ireland international who missed a vital kick in the shoot-out to decide the 1990 Scottish Cup Final?

8. Which Third Division side knocked Newcastle out of the 1992 FA Cup on penalties?

9. Who converted five penalties for Wimbledon in the 1991-92 First Division?

10. How many spot-kicks were Inter Milan awarded in their Italian League match against Verona in September 1991?

11. Who put Manchester City ahead in the 1981 FA Cup Final replay by firing home a second-half penalty?

12. Can you remember which goalkeeper saved a penalty during the 1988 Littlewoods Cup Final between Arsenal and Luton?

Long-Range Shot

13. What was coincidental about Blackpool winning the 1992 Fourth Division play-off on a penalty shoot-out?

14. What delayed the taking of Gerry Daly's penalty for Derby in the match against Manchester City in April 1977?

15. Who was the Dutchman who hit four penalty goals during the 1978 World Cup finals?

16. Can you name Spurs' goalkeeping hero of the 1984 UEFA Cup Final penalty shoot-out?

17. Peter Shilton only saved one penalty during his 125 game international career. Do you know who the penalty-taker was?

18. In November 1988, Argentinos Juniors eventually defeated Racing Club Avellaneda in the longest penalty shoot-out on record. What was the final result?

Sharp in the Box

Name the four countries who were eliminated from the 1990 World Cup finals by a penalty shoot-out.

QUIZ 37
QUITE A SEASON – 1989-90

'I enjoyed my first season back in England and was delighted to finish as the First Division's top scorer once again.'

Open Goal

1. Which crucial Football League matches were held at Wembley for the first time in May 1990?

2. What was the subject of the Taylor Report which was published in January?

3. Who moved for a world-record fee of £7.7 million in May?

4. Which new satellite TV station began broadcasting live football matches in April?

5. Which former Celtic idol made a dramatic return to Parkhead in the colours of Rangers in August 1989?

6. Which team won the Second Division play-offs but were denied promotion as a punishment for financial irregularities?

Half-Chance

7. Where did defending champions Arsenal crash to a 4-1 defeat on the opening Saturday of the 1989-90 season?

8. Who was the First Division player-manager who hit a hat trick at Villa Park in September?

9. Which city saw both of its clubs promoted from Division Three at the end of the season?

10. In September, Liverpool chalked up the biggest First Division victory since 1963. Which newly-promoted team did they thrash 9-0?

11. Which country ended England's 17-game unbeaten run by winning at Wembley in May?

12. Which club were banned from European competition for two seasons after missile-throwing by their fans during the UEFA Cup tie with Austria Vienna in October?

Long-Range Shot

13. Which London side went 20 matches without a win in the 1989-90 First Division?

14. Who scored four goals for Newcastle against Leeds on the opening day of the season?

15. Which trophy did Hereford United win?

16. Which Second Division team failed to score in 22 of their 46 League matches?

17. Aldershot drew 0-0 at Sheffield Wednesday in the first leg of the teams' second round Littlewoods Cup tie. What was the result of the second leg?

18. Can you remember which Belgian outfit dumped Hibs out of the 1989-90 UEFA Cup?

Sharp in the Box

Who were the managers of the top three teams in the 1989-90 First Division?

QUIZ 38
RECORD BREAKERS

'Although not all players might admit it, breaking a record does give a lot of satisfaction.'

Open Goal

1. Which goalkeeper became the first British player to appear in 1,000 first-class matches when he played for Arsenal against West Bromwich in February 1983?

2. Which team has won the FA Cup a record eight times?

3. Who in November 1983, became the first player to score 100 League goals for a single club in both Scotland and England?

4. Which club smashed the British transfer record for a defender when they bought Keith Curle from Wimbledon in July 1991?

5. Who is the youngest player ever to have appeared in the World Cup finals?

6. Can you name the Italian goalkeeper who set a new international clean sheet record during the 1990 World Cup?

Half-Chance

7. Which was the only club to play in all six divisions of the Football League between 1888 and 1992?

8. Can you name the Stockport County striker who, at 6' 7", was the League's tallest player in 1991-92?

9. Who is the only man to have been both England's and Scotland's Footballer of the Year?

10. In 1958, France's Just Fontaine set a new record for the

most goals in a single World Cup tournament. How many did he score?

11. Who was the only player to score a hat-trick in all four divisions of the Football League between 1958 and 1992?

12. Which team had the worst league record in British senior football in 1991-92?

Long-Range Shot

13. Who scored a British record 37 hat-tricks during his career at Tranmere, Everton and Notts County?

14. Rangers set a new Scottish Premier Division goals-for record in 1991-92. How many did they score 81, 91 or 101?

15. Which is the oldest international fixture in continental Europe?

16. Which team set an unenviable new record for successive penalty misses in October 1991?

17. Which ground holds the attendance record for a single Football League match?

18. Do you know the name of the Brazilian who is thought to be the world's leading goalscorer of all time?

Sharp in the Box

Can you name the players who broke the £1,000, £10,000 and £100,000 British transfer records respectively?

QUITE A SEASON – 1988-89

'I'm sure there'll never be such a dramatic end to a season as there was in 1989 when Arsenal clinched the League Championship in injury time at Anfield.'

Open Goal

1. Which team slammed Real Madrid 5-0 in the second leg of the 1988-89 European Cup semi-final?

2. Michael Thomas scored Arsenal's Championship-winning goal at Anfield, but who had headed them in front earlier in the match?

3. Which manager was charged by the FA after a violent incident with some of his own club's fans in January 1989?

4. Joe Miller's goal won the 1989 Scottish Cup Final for which club?

5. Who was the sports minister at the centre of controversy over his card-based membership scheme?

6. Graham Roberts hit twelve penalty goals for the 1989 Second Division Champions. Who were they?

Half-Chance

7. Which club did Jim Smith leave to take charge of Newcastle in December?

8. Who was ordered off during Wimbledon's pre-season friendly on the Isle of Wight?

9. Which Scottish team lost narrowly to Bayern Munich in the quarter-finals of the UEFA Cup?

10. Who moved from West Ham to Everton for £2.2 million before the start of the 1988-89 season?

11. Which team enjoyed cup victories of 5-0 and 6-0 over Birmingham City?

12. Which team reached the Littlewoods Cup Final for the second successive year in 1989?

Long-Range Shot

13. Which country won the gold medal in the 1988 Olympic football tournament in Seoul?

14. Which Premier League team did Rangers defeat 5-1 and 4-1 during 1988-89?

15. Which Arsenal player was given a nine-game ban for breaking the jaw of Southampton's Glenn Cockerill?

16. Who failed to turn up for Kevin Moran's testimonial match in August?

17. Do you know which team topped the First Division table on Christmas Day, 1988?

18. Which two clubs contested the Final of the Mercantile Credit Centenary Trophy at Villa Park in October?

Sharp in the Box

What were the results of the three 1989 Rous Cup matches involving England, Scotland and Chile?

QUIZ 40
SOCCER – THE WORLD GAME

'The advance which football is making in places like Japan and the USA really just confirms its position as the world's most popular sport.'

Open Goal

1. What international tournament did the Ivory Coast win in January 1992?

2. Which Blackburn Rovers striker was informed that he was part of the USA's World Cup team plans in May 1992?

3. Which prestigious international club match has been staged in Tokyo since 1980?

4. In what way will Detroit's Pontiac Silverdome break new ground in the 1994 World Cup finals?

5. Can you remember which Asian country shocked Italy with a 1-0 victory in the 1966 World Cup?

6. Who was the Marseille star who missed Ghana's appearance in the 1992 African Nations Cup Final after picking up a second yellow card in the semi-final?

Half-Chance

7. What is South America's equivalent of the European Championship called?

8. Which three countries did England play on their 1991 summer tour?

9. In which country does a team called Barcelona play at the Monumental?

10. Where was the first-ever Women's World Cup held in 1991?

11. In which year did New Zealand reach the World Cup finals?

12. Can you name the Chilean side who played in the 1991 World Club Championship match against Red Star Belgrade?

Long-Range Shot

13. The highest-ever official attendance at a club match was recorded at a 1963 derby game in Rio de Janeiro. 177,656 watched which two teams in opposition?

14. In which country does the team Hearts of Oak play?

15. Who is the Uruguayan-born midfielder who was the USA's top player in the 1990 World Cup finals?

16. Can you give the name of Morocco's leading army side?

17. Which country became a footballing *El Dorado* in the 1950s, after forming a pirate league outwith the jurisdiction of FIFA?

18. Who was the former Blackpool and England goalkeeper who, as national coach of Canada, took that country to their first-ever World Cup finals in 1986?

Sharp in the Box

Who were Asia's two representatives in the 1990 World Cup finals?

QUIZ 41
THE CHAMPIONS' CUP

'Despite tentative beginnings in the 1950s, the Champions' Cup is now clearly the ultimate prize in European club football.'

Open Goal

1. Which was the first English team to win the European Cup?

2. Where was the 1992 final held?

3. Ronald Koeman has now won European Cup medals with two clubs. Can you name them?

4. Who was the last Englishman to play in a European Cup final?

5. Which Czech side knocked both Rangers and Marseille out of the 1991-92 tournament?

6. In which city have Liverpool twice won the Cup?

Half-Chance

7. Which of the 1992 semi-finalists were unable to play any matches on their home ground?

8. Which was the last Final in which both teams scored?

9. Can you name the Yugoslavian coach who steered Sampdoria to the 1992 Final?

10. Which team has lost more European Cup Finals than any other side?

11. Who headed Nottingham Forest's winning goal in the 1979 Final against Malmo?

12. Which is the only team to have won the European Cup after a replay?

Long-Range Shot

13. Who scored Arsenal's goal in the 1-1 draw away to Benfica in the second round first leg tie of October 1991?

14. Who in 1991, became the first man to win a European Cup medal with two different clubs?

15. Can you name the manager who has taken Feyenoord, FC Bruges and SV Hamburg to European Cup Finals since 1970?

16. In the 1992 semi-finals, Benfica striker Sergei Yuran scored two goals against his old club. Who was that?

17. Which was the first team to win a European Cup tie on the toss of a coin?

18. Who once scored three goals in a European Cup Final but still finished on the losing side?

Sharp in the Box

Can you name the five teams which have won the European Cup at Wembley Stadium?

FUTBOL ESPAÑOL

*'My three years at Barcelona were a tremendous experience.
The fans there were great to me.'*

Open Goal

1. Name the manager who led Barcelona to European Cup success in 1992.

2. Can you name the flamboyant Mexican international striker who has been a big star of Spanish football since 1981?

3. Who were the 1992 champions of Spain?

4. In which colour of shirts does the national team play?

5. Which former Cardiff City and Liverpool star has managed both Real Madrid and Real Sociedad?

6. What is the name of Barcelona's magnificent home stadium?

Half-Chance

7. Which Red Star Belgrade midfielder joined Real Madrid for a reputed £2.5 million in the summer of 1991?

8. Who were the Canary Islands' representatives in the 1991-92 Spanish First Division?

9. For which Spanish club did John Aldridge play?

10. Can you name the Colombian World Cup captain who played in Spain for Valladolid during 1991-92?

11. What was the former name of Real Madrid's Bernabeu Stadium?

12. Who is the one-time Leicester City boss who managed Seville during 1986-87?

Long-Range Shot

13. Barcelona stars Zubizarreta and Alexanco were both signed from which Basque club?

14. Which Spanish club reached three consecutive Fairs Cup Finals during the 1960s?

15. Can you name the Atletico Madrid goalkeeper who set a new world shut-out record of 1,275 minutes in March 1991?

16. In which city do Real Betis play?

17. Who was the last Spaniard to be voted European Footballer of the Year?

18. Real Madrid's nursery side compete in the Spanish Second Division. What are they called?

Sharp in the Box

Between 1980 and 1992, German international Bernd Schuster played for three top Spanish clubs. Name them, in the order in which he joined them.

QUIZ 43
STARS OF EUROPE

'I've played with and against most of Europe's top stars of recent years. For me though, Michel Platini, with his delicate through passes, was simply a striker's dream.'

Open Goal

1. Which German star missed the 1992 European Championship after injuring his knee playing for Inter Milan against Parma in April?

2. Who is the classy sweeper who skippered AC Milan to the Italian League title in 1991-92?

3. The Laudrup brothers, Brian and Michael, are both internationalists for which country?

4. Who became the most expensive Bulgarian footballer of all time in 1990?

5. For which German *Bundesliga* team did Andy Moller star during 1991-92?

6. In which year did Michel Platini lead France to European Championship success?

Half-Chance

7. Can you name the Belgian international playmaker, born of Sicilian parents, who has played for both Inter Milan and Torino in Italy?

8. Which former Danish star was in charge of Bayern Munich for six months of the 1991-92 season?

9. Matthias Sammer won a *Bundesliga* championship medal

with which club in 1992?

10. Who is the former USSR World Cup veteran who managed the CIS team in the 1992 European Championship?

11. Stephane Chapuisat is an international striker for which country?

12. Which much-capped Belgian full-back captained PSV Eindhoven to an impressive 'Treble' of League, Cup and European Cup in 1988?

Long-Range Shot

13. Which Greek club signed Ukrainian star Oleg Protasov from Dynamo Kiev in 1990?

14. Can you name the Swiss international midfielder who is the world's most-capped outfield player?

15. Who kept goal for Sweden in the 1992 European Championship?

16. For which country does defender Gheorge Popescu play?

17. During the 1970s, who succeeded Johan Cruyff as captain of both Ajax and Holland?

18. Can you remember the name of the Bulgarian striker who scored for FC Porto against Spurs, in the 1991-92 European Cup-Winners' Cup second round first leg tie at White Hart Lane?

Sharp in the Box

Four Germans were voted European Footballer of the Year between 1970 and 1991. How many of them can you name?

QUIZ 44
THE CUP-WINNERS' CUP

_____

*'I was fortunate enough to win a medal in this competition
with Barca in 1989. We beat Sampdoria 2-0 in the Final in
Berne.'*

Open Goal

1. Which manager has led two different British clubs to
European Cup-Winners' Cup success?

2. Which German side won the 1992 tournament?

3. Who scored both goals as Sampdoria defeated Anderlecht
in the 1990 Cup-Winners' Cup Final?

4. Which team did Marco Van Basten captain in the 1987
Final?

5. Manchester United's run as Cup-Winners' Cup holders
ended when they lost to which Spanish team in the 1991-92
second round?

6. Who hit both of United's goals against Barcelona in the
1991 Final?

Half-Chance

7. Who did Rangers defeat to win the Cup-Winners' Cup in
1972?

8. Can you remember which former Spurs star played against
his old team in the 1991-92 tournament?

9. Where was the 1992 Final held?

10. Can you name the New Zealand international striker who
was on the scoresheet in that match?

11. Which club reached three consecutive Cup-Winners' Cup Finals during the 1970s?

12. In the first round of the 1991-92 tournament, Swansea incurred the heaviest defeat ever sustained by a Welsh club in European competition. What was the aggregate score of their tie against Monaco?

Long-Range Shot

13. Who were England's first representatives in the European Cup-Winners' Cup?

14. Which team knocked European debutants Motherwell out of the 1991-92 competition?

15. Can you remember who scored Spurs' decisive second goal in the return leg of their 1991 first round tie with Hajduk Split?

16. Which club won the Cup-Winners' Cup at Wembley in 1965?

17. Which was the last club to win the tournament who were not the holders of their own national cup?

18. Manchester United's 1991-92 conquerors, Atletico Madrid, eventually lost themselves in the quarter-finals. Which team ousted them on the away goals rule?

Sharp in the Box

A Scotsman, an Englishman and an Irishman were all on the scoresheet in Everton's 1985 Cup-Winners' Cup Final victory over Rapid Vienna. Can you name the players concerned?

QUIZ 45
CALCIO – THE ITALIAN LEAGUE

'Although I have never played club football in Italy, I do rate their football highly – there are so many quality players.'

Open Goal

1. What impressive new record did AC Milan set while winning the 1991-92 Italian League?

2. Which Italian club signed England's Des Walker in the summer of 1992?

3. At which club did German stars Thomas Hassler and Rudi Voller play together during 1991-92?

4. In which city do Lazio play?

5. Which team is known as *'La Vecchia Signora'* (The Old Lady) of Italian football?

6. For years in Italy, there has been dispute over the number of *stranieri* which should be allowed in each team. What are they?

Half-Chance

7. Who took Maradona's No. 10 shirt and replaced him as Napoli's star playmaker?

8. Which team won the 1992 Italian Cup with a surprise aggregate victory over Juventus?

9. Can you name the two Germans who starred for Lazio during 1991-92?

10. In 1992, which leading Italian club failed to secure a

European place for the first time in 17 seasons?

11. Brazilian free-kick specialist Branco joined which *Serie A* club in November 1990?

12. Known as 'Trap', this top coach moved from Inter to Juventus in the summer of 1991. Who is he?

Long-Range Shot

13. Which was the last Sardinian club to win the *Serie A*?

14. Who were the two Englishmen signed by Bari for £800,000 in June 1985?

15. Who competes for the Italian Super Cup?

16. Talented midfield star Gianni Rivera was which club's most popular player during the 1960s and '70s?

17. Which was the last team to win the Italian 'Double'?

18. What was unusual about Michaelangelo Rampulla's headed equalizer for Cremonese against Atalanta in February 1992?

Sharp in the Box

Name the six Italian clubs which have played in the European Cup Final since 1956.

THE UEFA CUP

'In some ways, the UEFA Cup can be the hardest of all the European tournaments. There are more rounds to play and so many strong teams.'

Open Goal

1. Who won the 1992 UEFA Cup?

2. In what way does the UEFA Cup Final differ from the European Cup and Cup-Winners' Cup Finals?

3. Can you name the two English clubs which won the competition during the 1980s?

4. Which is the only Scots club to have played in the Final – Aberdeen or Dundee United?

5. Since 1958, which country's teams have won this tournament (under its various labels) more often – England's or Italy's?

6. Who was Liverpool's manager when The Reds first won the UEFA Cup?

Half-Chance

7. Name the Brazilian who scored twice for Torino in the first leg of the 1992 Final.

8. Which was the last part-time club to win the tournament?

9. Celtic's 1991-92 first round opponents, Germinal Ekeren, hail from which country?

10. Who broke Roger Hunt's record of seven goals in a single European campaign for Liverpool, when he netted a hat-trick

against FC Tirol in the 1991-92 third round second leg match?

11. German international striker Jurgen Klinsmann won a UEFA Cup runners-up medal with which club in 1989?

12. Which Scot scored 14 goals in the 1980-81 tournament?

Long-Range Shot

13. What was the full original title of the competition which eventually became the UEFA Cup?

14. Which Torino player helped eliminate his old club Real Madrid in the 1992 semi-finals?

15. With which club did South Korea's Cha Bum Kun win a UEFA Cup medal in 1988?

16. Do you know the name of the Englishman who scored against Liverpool in the 1991-92 competition?

17. Which was the last team to win the UEFA Cup in successive seasons?

18. In the 1970-71 Fairs Cup tournament, a team played out twelve matches undefeated yet still failed to lift the trophy. Who were they?

Sharp in the Box

Three clubs have now won all three major European club trophies. Can you name them?

THE FRENCH CONNECTION

'France has produced some very talented footballers despite, in my opinion, having a relatively weak domestic league.

Open Goal

1. How much did Marseille pay Rangers for Trevor Steven in 1991: £3 million, £4 million or £5 million?

2. Which French team lost in the 1992 European Cup-Winners' Cup Final?

3. Who is the flamboyant millionaire head of Adidas who bought control of Olympic Marseille in 1986?

4. What is the chief venue used by the French national team for their home matches?

5. In February 1992, England became the first country to beat France in 19 internationals. Which had been the last team to defeat them, in March 1989?

6. Where in France was there a tragic crowd accident involving a temporary stand in May 1992?

Half-Chance

7. For which French club did Mo Johnston play?

8. Diminutive Rui Barros, who joined Monaco from Juventus in 1990, is an internationalist for which country?

9. Which French team are known as 'Les Verts' (The Greens)?

10. Who was the former Arsenal star who played for Le Havre during 1991-92?

11. Which French side did Manchester United defeat in the

quarter-finals of the 1991 European Cup-Winners' Cup?

12. In which year did Glenn Hoddle and Mark Hateley win a French League Championship medal with Monaco?

Long-Range Shot

13. Can you name the Yugoslav who coached Marseille to the 1992 Championship?

14. Where was France's uncompromising defender Basile Boli actually born?

15. For which club have Britons Eric Black and David Hodgson played?

16. Known as 'Manu', this son of a Spanish immigrant has won Championship medals with Monaco and Marseille and has been a regular in the French international team since 1982. Who is he?

17. For which club side did Christian Perez star during 1991-92?

18. In which French First Division stadium is there a spectators' car park underneath the pitch?

Sharp in the Box

Three French teams have played in the European Cup Final. Can you name them?

CONTINENTAL HIT-MEN

'It's a tough job scoring goals in Europe's top leagues. You have to admire the men who do it regularly.'

Open Goal

1. Which sportswear company traditionally awarded a 'Golden Boot' to Europe's leading league goalscorer?

2. By what nickname is Italian star striker Salvatore Schillaci usually known?

3. Which top French marksman moved from Marseille to Milan in the summer of 1992?

4. What was the nickname of the 1970s German goal getter Gerd Muller?

5. Who was the leading scorer in the 1991-92 Italian *Serie A*?

6. Can you name the Yugoslav who was the top scorer in the qualifying matches for the 1992 European Championship?

Half-Chance

7. Dennis Bergkamp's goals helped which team to European trophy success in 1992?

8. Which club was Hristo Stoichkov playing for when he won the 1990 Golden Boot award?

9. Which powerfully-built striker became the most expensive Finnish player of all time when he moved from Dundee United to Aberdeen for £400,000 in March 1992?

10. Luc Nilis and Johnny Bosman scored over 30 goals between them in the 1991-92 Belgian League. For which club were they on target?

11. Can you name the now-retired FC Bruges striker who hit 23 goals in a record 96 appearances for the Belgian national team?

12. Who was the Swedish international hit-man who was injured in the closing minutes of the 1992 UEFA Cup Final?

Long-Range Shot

13. Which member of West Germany's 1980 European Championship winning team succeeded Ernst Happel as manager of Austrian side FC Tirol in 1992?

14. Which leading European striker often performs at anti-apartheid concerts with his band Revelation Time?

15. For which club was Ghanaian international striker Anthony Yeboah regularly on target during the 1991-92 German *Bundesliga*?

16. He has played for Torino, Ascoli, Seville and Logrones and his hat-trick against East Germany clinched Austria's place in the 1990 World Cup finals. Who is he?

17. Which Turkish former Golden Boot winner caused a sensation in the summer of 1991 when he left Istanbul's Galatasaray for their deadly local rivals Fenerbahce?

18. Why was Dynamo Dresden's 1991 East German Footballer of the Year, Torsten Gutschow, at the centre of a political controversy in January 1992?

Sharp in the Box

Rangers' Ally McCoist was Europe's top league goal-scorer in 1991-92. Name the three other Scots who also finished in the top three of the Euro scoring charts between 1968 and 1983.

QUIZ 49
SPORTING SOCCER FANS

'Like so many other sportsmen, my good friend, snooker star Willie Thorne is a football nut.'

Open Goal

1. Which world-famous golfer was at Wembley to cheer on Barcelona in the 1992 European Cup final?

2. Which of the Merseyside teams does snooker ace John Parrott follow?

3. This Dundee United fan became the women's 10,000 metre world champion in August 1991. Who is she?

4. Which London club does former Olympic star Seb Coe support?

5. Which of Coe's old 1500 metre rivals was at Wembley to cheer on Sunderland in the FA Cup Final against Liverpool?

6. Hearts can include the 1992 world snooker champion amongst their supporters. Who is he?

Half-Chance

7. Which is the favourite football team of swimmer Zara Long and tennis commentator Gerry Williams?

8. Which England cricket captain is a fan of West Ham?

9. Which club does athlete David Moorcroft follow?

10. Snooker's Jimmy White and darts star Eric Bristow are both fans of which team?

11. Why has Steve Davis had to travel more than most to watch his favourite team in recent seasons?

12. Can you name the BBC racing commentator who has been a keen follower of Swindon Town for many years?

Long-Range Shot

13. Which is the favourite football team of former British tennis star John Lloyd?

14. This Chelsea supporter has played both Rugby Union and Rugby League for Wales. Who is he?

15. Boxer Pat Clinton used the facilities of his favourite football club to train for his 1992 world flyweight title fight. Which club was this?

16. Irish snooker player Alex Higgins is a fan of which club?

17. Former Wimbledon champion Stefan Edberg claims to be a supporter of which English team?

18. Can you name Channel Four's extrovert racing pundit who follows Newcastle United?

Sharp in the Box

England Under-21 international Ian Brightwell is the son of two former British Olympic athletes. Can you name them?

READ ALL ABOUT IT

'I can hardly keep up with all the soccer books and magazines on the market now – the fans certainly can't complain about a shortage of reading material.'

Open Goal

1. Which is Britain's oldest weekly soccer magazine?

2. Rob Bishop's book *Bully* is the biography of which star striker?

3. Supporters of which club produce the fanzines *An Imperfect Match* and *The Gooner*?

4. In which country is there a football magazine called *Kicker*?

5. Who wrote the book entitled *It's a Funny Old Life*?

6. Which particular type of players are the subject of Bob Wilson's book *You've Got To Be Crazy*?

Half-Chance

7. In which comic does the football character 'Billy the Fish' appear?

8. What is Britain's biggest-selling football club newspaper?

9. Can you name the writer, a connoisseur of Italian football, who joined the *People* in 1992 after 33 years with the *Sunday Times*?

10. Who is the subject of the book *Rough at the Top*?

11. Which former England manager's autobiography is entitled *Against The Odds*?

12. In which country could you buy the daily football and

sports paper called *Marca*?

Long-Range Shot

13. To what does the book *The Glory, Glory Nights* refer?
14. Name the FA coach who wrote the book *The Winning Formula*.
15. Which club is the subject of Jeff Kent's *The Valiants' Years*?
16. Who is featured in the book *Green Gunners*?
17. What is Italy's leading daily sports paper?
18. What witty title did Stuart Cosgrove give to his book on scandal in Scottish football?

Sharp in the Box

What is the derivation of the St Johnstone fanzine title *Wendy Who?*?

HOWZAT! FOOTBALLING CRICKETERS

---

*'I showed a lot of promise as a cricketer at school but, in the end,
I had to decide to concentrate on my football.'*

Open Goal

1. Which West Indian cricket star played for Antigua in the qualifying tournament for the 1978 soccer World Cup?

2. Which Scottish international goalkeeper has represented his country in the NatWest trophy?

3. For which Football League club did Ian Botham play?

4. Which member of England's 1966 World Cup winning team was also an occasional first-class cricketer with Essex?

5. Steve Gatting, who has played for Arsenal, Brighton and Charlton, is the brother of which famous cricketer?

6. Which Test cricket ground staged the first-ever FA Cup Final in 1872?

Half-Chance

7. Which distinguished Test batsman won an FA Cup winners medal with Arsenal in 1950?

8. Who kept goal for Aston Villa's 1975 League Cup winning side, the year after he had helped Worcester take the County Championship?

9. Which former England cricket captain first played League football for Bradford City in 1952?

10. He won a League Championship medal with Arsenal and

109

later managed Chelsea to the title. He also played county cricket for Hampshire – who is he?

11. Which ground staged Test and county cricket until 1973 before the resident football club built a new stand on top of the cricket pitch?

12. Who's sporting career includes football for Sheffield Wednesday, Celtic and the Republic of Ireland along with cricket honours for Cornish schools?

Long-Range Shot

13. England cricket manager Mickey Stewart turned professional with which soccer club in 1956?

14. Who skippered both Lincoln City and Worcester CCC during 1982-83?

15. Which Rangers manager of the 1950s and '60s was capped five times by the Scotland cricket team?

16. Who played Fourth Division football (for Doncaster Rovers) and County Championship cricket (for Leicestershire) on the same day in September 1975?

17. Can you name Woking's FA Cup hero of January 1991 who has represented Gibraltar at cricket?

18. The Glasgow ground of West of Scotland CC staged the first-ever Scotland-England soccer international in 1872. Can you name it?

Sharp in the Box

Football borrowed the expression 'hat-trick' from cricket. Do you know the origin of the term?

THE COLOURS

'Strips change a lot more often than they used to. For instance, I must have worn about three different designs of England jersey during my career.'

Open Goal

1. In what colour of jerseys did England win the World Cup in 1966?

2. What are the colours of West Ham?

3. Name the only English Premier League side who play in hooped jerseys.

4. In what colour of strip did Manchester United win the FA Cup in 1948, the European Cup in 1968 and the Rumbelows Cup in 1992?

5. Which of the teams wore alternative kits in the 1992 European Cup Final between Barcelona and Sampdoria?

6. Can you name the two Scottish Premier League sides who play in green and white strips?

Half-Chance

7. Which leading English First Division side wore numbered stocking tabs during the early 1970s?

8. In what colours did Sunderland contest the 1992 FA Cup Final?

9. Which sportswear firm supplies the kit for all four British international teams?

10. Can you remember the colours of Manchester United's

1991 European Cup-Winners' Cup opponents Athinaikos?

11. In August 1991, which First Division club's new 'away' jersey was likened to a 'bruised banana'?

12. What are Darlington's colours?

Long-Range Shot

13. Which shirt number has been labelled 'unlucky' at Leeds United?

14. What was the most popular colour for an 'away' strip in the 1991-92 First Division?

15. In 1961, which Scottish Second Division club changed their colours to yellow and red because their old blue and white strip looked 'too much like Rangers'?

16. Why was Sampdoria's match at Lazio in May 1992 a 'game of two halves' as far as their kit was concerned?

17. What are the colours of *Bundesliga* team Borussia Moenchengladbach?

18. George Graham tried to stop Arsenal's players doing it after their 1991 European Cup tie against Austria Vienna and Alf Ramsey stopped the England team doing it with the Argentinians in 1966 – what?

Sharp in the Box

Since 1970, the England national side has played in four different colours of jerseys. What are they?

QUIZ 53
YOU MUST BE JOKING!

'Every dressing room has its fair share of jokers. At Spurs, there was never a dull moment with the likes of Gazza about.'

Open Goal

1. Who came up with the legendary quote: 'Football's not a matter of life and death – it's more important than that'?

2. Which much-maligned midfielder said: 'The last time anyone said "good pass" was when I handed over my UB40 to the lady at the dole office'?

3. Which manager declared in the summer of 1991: 'I'd be bananas to walk away from a club like Sheffield Wednesday'?

4. Who did Brian Clough say would decide whether or not his son and star striker Nigel would be leaving Nottingham Forest for Italy?

5. Who quipped, after scoring the Rangers goal which beat Celtic in the 1992 Scottish Cup semi-final: 'Celtic said when they beat us last week that it was their easiest game of the season. Well, I hope that was their second-easiest game!'?

6. Which TV star talked philosophically about supporting Birmingham when he said: 'You lose some, you draw some'?

Half-Chance

7. During the 1991-92 season, which comedian and Liverpool fan joked: 'Any more knocks and we'll be sponsored by BUPA next year!'?

8. Which manager had a dig at UEFA's four foreigners per team ruling when he said: 'I never thought I'd see the day when a Scotsman would say that he needed to find more Englishmen!'?

9. Who complained, after an energetic World Cup qualifying match for the Republic of Ireland: 'Much more of this and our legs will be worn down to stumps!'?

10. Which former Newcastle star said scathingly of his old club: 'I've heard of players selling dummies, but this club keeps buying them!'?

11. Who said, after being sacked as QPR boss in 1991: 'I can see now why Terry Venables wants to buy his own club'?

12. Which Republic of Ireland defender said: 'When Ruud Gullit pulls on my shirt at home, he'll wonder who the hell's it is'?

Long-Range Shot

13. Which realist of a manager said in 1991: 'Every club I've been at, the chairman gives me £50,000 and says "go on a spending spree"!'?

14. What were West Brom's John Trewick's observations on the Great Wall of China, during Albion's 1978 tour of that country?

15. Who said, on hearing that Charlie Nicholas was leaving Arsenal in 1988,: 'Stringfellows will miss him!'?

16. Why did Stoke City striker John Ritchie voice his opposition to Sunday football in 1974?

17. Which BBC commentator came up with this classic: 'For the benefit of those watching in black and white, Spurs are in the yellow shirts!'?

18. Which manager moaned: 'Nowadays, goalkeepers are a more protected species than the Golden Eagle'?

Sharp in the Box

Which controversial ex-manager joked: 'I've had more clubs than Jack Nicklaus' and 'I've been in more courts than Bjorn Borg'?

QUIZ 54
THE SONG REMAINS THE SAME

'I'm always amazed at the repertoire of songs that the supporters have. It gives players a lift to hear their name being sung.'

Open Goal

1. Which Gerry and the Pacemakers' hit was first adopted by Liverpool's Kop choir during the 1960s?

2. Which band teamed up with the England World Cup squad to make 'World in Motion' a number one record in 1990?

3. Can you remember which opera star had a hit with the World Cup theme tune 'Nessun Dorma'?

4. What is the Victorian hymn traditionally sung by the Wembley crowd before the FA Cup Final?

5. 'I'm Forever Blowing Bubbles' is the anthem of which club's fans?

6. Who sang a solo part in 'Ossie's Dream' in 1981?

Half-Chance

7. What's the next line of Leeds' 1972 record which begins: 'We play all the way for Leeds United ...'?

8. Which club's fans sing the Pompey chimes?

9. Can you name the Sandpipers' 1966 hit which has become a popular tune for football fans wishing to highlight the uniqueness of a particular player?

10. Which Spurs record refers to the coincidental connection

between the date and Tottenham's trophy successes?

11. Who had a 1991 hit with the football fans' favourite 'Always Look on the Bright Side of Life'?

12. Name the old song which has become the adopted anthem of Bristol Rovers supporters.

Long-Range Shot

13. What was the title of Crystal Palace's 1990 Cup Final record?

14. Can you name the Beautiful South vocalist who has an extensive collection of Italian football jerseys?

15. Which Glasgow club's song begins: 'Hail, Hail ...'?

16. Why is 'Simply Red' an appropriate title for singer Mick Hucknall's band?

17. Which Des O'Connor hit did Liverpool's Kop unkindly sing to Leeds goalkeeper Gary Sprake after he had thrown the ball into his own net?

18. Who is the Scotland penalty-taker referred to in the lyrics of their 1982 World Cup record 'We Have a Dream'?

Sharp in the Box

In 1982, who appeared on Top of the Pops with both the Spurs' FA Cup Final team and the Scotland World Cup squad?

QUIZ 55
SOCCER ON THE BOX

*'The increase in 'live' matches and the advent of satellite TV
have meant a real bonanza for armchair fans lately.'*

Open Goal

1. Which BBC highlights programme was first broadcast in
1964?

2. Which former West Ham and England midfielder often co-
commentates on England matches alongside John Motson?

3. Since regular 'live' broadcast of League games began in
1983, which team has been featured most often?

4. With which club did BBC presenter Bob Wilson win League
Championship and FA Cup medals?

5. Which former TV commentator's most famous line is 'They
think it's all over ... it is now!'?

6. Which of the TV companies followed Liverpool in Europe
during 1991-92?

Half-Chance

7. Can you name the BSkyB commentator who once played
for Corinthian Casuals?

8. During the 1980s, which England star could be seen on TV
advertising *Brut* men's cosmetics?

9. Which satellite TV channel covered the 1992 African
Nations Cup competition?

10. John Barnes took charge of one of the teams in *A Question of
Sport* during 1992. Which footballer did he replace as captain?

11. Who commentated on the 1992 European Cup Final for BBC?

12. TV commentator Alan Parry is a director of which Vauxhall Conference club?

Long-Range Shot

13. In which year were the World Cup finals first shown 'live' on British television?

14. Can you name the former Brookside actor who presents the fanzine-style football programme *Standing Room Only*?

15. Which non-League side does John Motson follow?

16. Name the BBC Scotland commentator who played in three successive Cambridge v Oxford university matches during the 1960s.

17. Which former Liverpool and Republic of Ireland striker became a football commentator on Spanish television?

18. During the 1990 World Cup finals, how many hours of football per day were broadcast by the Brazilian TV station Manchete?

Sharp in the Box

During the 1991-92 season, Sky Sports showed 'live' domestic football from which four countries?

STRANGE BUT TRUE?

---

*'Soccer certainly throws up some oddities from time to time.
See if you can separate the fact from the fiction...'*

Open Goal

1. True or false: Allan Hansen was Europe's fourth highest goalscorer in the 1981-82 season?

2. Which Liverpool megastar of the 1970s and '80s failed to impress the club during a trial for their 'B' team against Southport in 1966?

3. True or false: a Swedish-born player has captained teams in both the Scottish and English FA Cup Finals since 1987?

4. What is Mark Walters' totally-inappropriate middle name?

5. True or false: Crewe take the 'Alexandra' part of their name from Princess Alexandra?

6. Can you name the Wimbledon champion who had trials with Bayern Munich as a youngster?

Half-Chance

7. Which England international striker allegedly made 34 transfer requests during his time at QPR?

8. How could a team lose a match in the 1945-46 FA Cup yet still progress in the tournament?

9. Who was the Airdrie captain who missed the 1992 Scottish Cup Final after being booked for 'pulling a face' in the semi-final?

10. Can you name the former Sunderland striker who was the

Liberal Democrats' candidate for Sunderland North in the 1992 General Election?

11. Manchester United's European Cup Final goalkeeper once dislocated his jaw while shouting at his defenders. Who is he?

12. Which country failed to get a single shot at England's goal during a 1971 European Championship match at Wembley?

Long-Range Shot

13. How many players called Jones were on Charlton's books in the 1966-67 season?

14. Why were Liberia's players pleased with their goal-less draw against Gambia in 1980?

15. Which Scottish First Division team are nicknamed 'The Blue Brazil'?

16. How many linesmen should officiate at a football match, according to QPR boss Gerry Francis?

17. Why did Ipswich players wear special contact lenses in some matches during 1991-92?

18. What ended the football career of Brentford goalkeeper Chic Brodie in 1970?

Sharp in the Box

In every season between 1985 and 1988, the Footballer of the Year was on the losing side in the FA Cup Final. Gary was one (in 1986), can you name the other three?

ANSWERS TO QUIZ 1
THE LEAGUE CHAMPIONSHIP

1. Bramall Lane, Sheffield United
2. Two
3. Liverpool
4. Nottingham Forest
5. Matt Busby
6. Gordon Strachan

7. Everton
8. Peter Withe
9. John Lukic and Gary McAllister
10. Derby County
11. Burnley
12. The 1930s

13. Preston
14. Six
15. Chelsea, in 1955
16. Huddersfield
17. Ipswich Town
18. Alf Ramsey

Sharp in the box

Manchester United, Liverpool, Everton, Arsenal and Derby.

ANSWERS TO QUIZ 2
UPS AND DOWNS

1. Luton Town
2. Blackburn
3. Sheffield Wednesday
4. John Lyall
5. Blackburn
6. Denis Law's

7. Oldham
8. Lincoln City
9. Lou Macari
10. Wolves
11. Charlton
12. Nottingham Forest

13. 1973-74
14. Grimsby
15. 'Test Matches'
16. Preston North End
17. Notts County
18. They had been Champions in the previous season

Sharp in the Box

Barnet, Maidstone, Scarborough and Wigan

ANSWERS TO QUIZ 3
THE FA CUP

1. Ian Rush
2. Bobby Robson
3. Manchester United and Crystal Palace (1990)
4. Michael Thomas
5. Dave Beasant
6. Portsmouth

7. Terry Venables
8. Wrexham
9. Norman Whiteside
10. Paul Bracewell
11. Manchester United
12. One (John Aldridge v Everton in 1989)

13. Willie Young
14. Brighton
15. Phil Don
16. Bob Stokoe and Don Revie
17. Leicester (1961), Sunderland (1973) and Crystal Palace (1990)
18. Liverpool's Craig Johnston, who took it to Australia to show his family

---

Sharp in the Box

Matt Busby, Tommy Docherty, Dave Sexton, Ron Atkinson and Alex Ferguson

---

ANSWERS TO QUIZ 4
TO HULL AND BACK

1. Aldershot
2. Denis Law
3. John Bond
4. Carlisle United
5. Scunthorpe
6. Swansea

7. John Chiedozie
8. Doncaster Rovers
9. Brentford
10. After the crooked spire near their ground
11. Bury
12. Tony Cascarino

13. Darlington
14. Dario Gradi
15. Blackpool
16. Hull
17. Stockport County
18. Reading

Sharp in the Box

Blackburn, Bristol Rovers, Doncaster, Tranmere, Albion and Raith

SCOTTISH FOOTBALL

1. Ally McCoist
2. Hibs
3. Liam Brady
4. Airdrie
5. Tangerine and black
6. Celtic, Rangers and Partick Thistle

7. Alex Smith
8. Rangers
9. Dundee
10. Tony Mowbray
11. St Mirren
12. Paul and Willie McStay (Celtic, 1985)

13. Kilmarnock
14. Alexei Mikhailichenko and Oleg Kuznetsov
15. Hamilton Accies
16. Sandy Jardine
17. Aberdeen
18. Jim Farry

Sharp in the Box

Celtic, Clyde, Clydebank and Cowdenbeath

THE FOOTBALL LEAGUE CUP

1. Nottingham Forest
2. Clive Allen
3. Littlewoods
4. Wolves
5. Ron Atkinson
6. Brian McClair

7. Kenny Dalglish
8. Peterborough
9. John Harkes
10. Old Trafford
11. Middlesbrough
12. A bomb scare

13. Alan Hardaker
14. Rochdale
15. Tommy Docherty
16. Kevin Gallacher and Nigel Clough
17. Birmingham
18. George Courtney

Sharp in the Box

Norwich (1962), QPR (1967), Swindon (1969), Aston Villa (1975), Sheffield Wednesday (1991)

IN A DIFFERENT LEAGUE

1. Colchester United
2. Martin O'Neill
3. Accrington Stanley
4. Diadora
5. Wimbledon
6. The winning of both the FA Trophy and Vauxhall Conference

7. Merthyr Tydfil (presently playing in the Conference)
8. Mark Carter
9. Gretna
10. Blyth Spartans
11. Non-League sides who are ineligible to compete in the FA Trophy
12. Telford United

13. Spurs in 1901
14. Hayes
15. Ted Croker
16. Valley Sports
17. The Highland League
18. Bishop's Stortford

Sharp in the Box

Altrincham, Boston United, Kettering Town, Northwich Victoria and Telford United

---

ANSWERS TO QUIZ 8
OTHER TOURNAMENTS

1. The League Champions and the FA Cup winners
2. Scot Gemmill
3. Cardiff Arms Park (also known as the National Stadium)
4. Sampdoria
5. Stoke City
6. The teams share the trophy

7. The Watney Cup
8. It was open to the two highest-scoring sides in each division (apart from those competing in Europe)
9. Wayne Clarke
10. Cardiff City
11. Nottingham Forest (who beat Ipswich 5-0)
12. Lee Chapman and Tony Cottee

13. They complained that the competing English teams were not strong enough despite the fact that only one Scottish side had ever won it!
14. Tranmere and Newcastle
15. A once-played two-legged competition for the two lower division clubs which progressed furthest in the FA Cup (Chester beat Port Vale in the one and only Final in 1977)
16. Pat Jennings
17. Airdrie
18. Burnley and Wolves

Sharp in the Box

Chelsea, Blackburn Rovers, Reading, Nottingham Forest and Crystal Palace

---

COME ON YOU SPURS

1. The UEFA Cup
2. Ricky Villa and Ossie Ardiles
3. Justin Edinburgh
4. A cockerel
5. Steve Perryman
6. FC Porto

7. Crystal Palace
8. They replaced their navy shorts and socks with an all-white strip.
9. Paul Gascoigne
10. Alf Ramsey
11. Aston Villa
12. Danny Blanchflower

13. 1977-78
14. Ian Walker
15. An FA XI
16. Keflavik
17. Arthur Rowe
18. 15th

Sharp in the Box

Paul Allen (West Ham), Gary Lineker and Pat Van den Hauwe (Everton)

MY STRIKING PARTNERS

1. Mark Hughes
2. Chelsea
3. Alan Smith
4. Scotland
5. Steve Bull
6. Peter Beardsley

7. Kerry Dixon
8. Oldham
9. 'Juke-box'
10. Paulo Futre
11. Bayern Munich
12. Four

13. 1986
14. Jim Melrose
15. Espanol
16. Julio Salinas
17. Gordon Durie
18. Alvechurch

Sharp in the Box

Carlisle, Manchester United, Newcastle, Liverpool and Everton

---

SOCCER IN THE MIDLANDS

1. Aston Villa
2. The City Ground
3. Derby
4. Terry Cooper
5. Blue
6. Coventry

7. Aston Villa
8. Billy Wright
9. Notts County
10. Derek Mountfield
11. Nacional
12. Derek Dougan

13. Nigel Gleghorn
14. Mansfield
15. Jeff Astle and Tony Brown
16. Walsall
17. Gordon Banks
18. Algeria

Sharp in the Box

Colin Todd (Derby), Andy Gray (Aston Villa), Peter Shilton (Nottingham Forest), David Platt (Aston Villa)

ANSWERS TO QUIZ 12
THE CAPTAINS

1. Holland
2. Stuart Pearce
3. Rangers
4. Bobby Moore
5. Bryan Robson
6. Dino Zoff

7. West Ham
8. Gerry Francis
9. Billy McNeill (Celtic)
10. Emlyn Hughes
11. Aberdeen and Manchester United
12. Tony Adams

13. 20
14. Ron Yeats
15. Ray Wilkins (who had taken over from the injured Bryan Robson during the 1986 World Cup)
16. Arsenal
17. Horatio
18. He was England's first-ever international captain

Sharp in the Box

Billy Wright, Bill Slater, Billy Bremner, Billy Bonds

THE PRIDE OF MERSEYSIDE

1. Kenny Dalglish
2. 'The Toffees'
3. Tranmere Rovers
4. Phil Neal
5. Everton
6. Liverpool

7. Martin Keown
8. Istvan Kozma
9. Chelsea
10. John King
11. Club Bruges and Borussia Moenchengladbach
12. David Johnson

13. Steve Nicol
14. John Ebbrell
15. Frank McGarvey
16. Ray Wilson (Everton) and Roger Hunt (Liverpool)
17. Norwich
18. Terry McDermott (Liverpool) and Gary Stanley (Everton)

Sharp in the Box

Harry Catterick, Billy Bingham, Gordon Lee, Howard Kendall and Colin Harvey

---

ANSWERS TO QUIZ 14
IRISH CREAM

1. Arsenal
2. John Aldridge
3. Arsenal and Manchester United
4. Roy Keane
5. John Byrne
6. Aston Villa

7. Scotland
8. John Sheridan
9. West Ham
10. Terry Mancini
11. Mick McCarthy
12. West Bromwich Albion

13. West Ham, Fulham and Oxford
14. 1989
15. Chris Hughton
16. Wales
17. Russian
18. Dr. Kevin O'Flanagan

Sharp in the Box

Spain, Denmark, Northern Ireland, Albania, Lithuania and Latvia

ANSWERS TO QUIZ 15
THE MEN WHO KEEP THEM OUT

1. Arsenal
2. Peter Shilton
3. Tony Norman
4. Bruce Grobbelaar
5. Danish
6. Liverpool and Spurs

7. Dundee
8. Les Sealey
9. Colombia
10. Chris Turner
11. Plymouth Argyle
12. They both played for Glasgow's Old Firm rivals – Ireland's Bonner for Celtic and England's Woods for Rangers

13. Spink, Rimmer (Villa) and Muller (Bayern)
14. 15
15. Torquay
16. Ally Maxwell
17. He was concussed and unable to take his place in goal
18. They put chewing gum on their hands to improve their grip

---

Sharp in the Box

Nottingham Forest, QPR, Norwich and Sheffield Wednesday

ANSWERS TO QUIZ 16
OH GARY, GARY...

1. Gary Gillespie
2. Everton
3. Gary Pallister
4. Gary Shaw
5. Leicester and Motherwell
6. Garry Birtles

7. Barnet
8. Gary Bailey
9. Gary Speed
10. Gary Ablett
11. St Johnstone and Hearts
12. Gary Penrice

13. Falkirk
14. Gary Kelly
15. Joanne Conway
16. Hereford United
17. Gary Brooke
18. David Speedie

Sharp in the Box

Gary Charles, Gary Crosby and Garry Parker

SWEDEN '92

1. Germany
2. Holland
3. Tomas Brolin
4. Gothenburg
5. David Platt
6. Yugoslavia

7. Brian McClair
8. Two
9. Rudi Voller
10. Malmo
11. Richard Gough
12. Michel Platini (France)

13. David Batty
14. Seven
15. Richard Moller-Nielson
16. Apart from the goalkeeper, the players were numbered in an order of seniority based on the amount of caps won
17. Karlheinz Riedle
18. Swiss

Sharp in the Box

Holland and Germany

WORLD CUP '86

1. Diego Maradona
2. The Azteca
3. Poland
4. Pat Jennings
5. Gary Stevens (of Everton and Spurs respectively)
6. Gordon Strachan

7. Mark Hateley and Ray Wilkins
8. Italy v France; France won 2-0
9. Morocco
10. Spurs
11. Toni Schumacher
12. A dislocated shoulder

13. The USSR, who beat Hungary 6-0
14. Bellone's shot rebounded from the post and technically should have been declared 'dead' before it hit Brazilian goalkeeper Carlos and bounced into the net
15. Pique
16. Paraguay
17. 'The Group of Death'
18. George Courtney

Sharp in the Box

Gary Bailey and Bryan Robson (England); Arthur Albiston and Gordon Strachan (Scotland); Norman Whiteside (N.Ireland); John Sivebaek and Jesper Olsen (Denmark)

ENGLAND'S LIONS

1. Alan Smith and Paul Merson
2. Paul Gascoigne
3. Bobby and Jack Charlton
4. John Barnes
5. He was the only player from a Second Division club
6. Butcher, Robson and Shilton

7. Trevor Steven
8. 'Butch'
9. Nobby Stiles
10. Mick Channon
11. Four
12. Chris Waddle

13. 53
14. Arsenal
15. Colin Viljoen
16. Tom Finney
17. QPR and Manchester City
18. Tony Adams

Sharp in the Box

Tony Dorigo and David Batty

ANSWERS TO QUIZ 20
WORLD CUP '90

---

1. Franz Beckenbauer
2. Italy
3. Frank Rijkaard and Rudi Voller
4. Mark Wright
5. Costa Rica
6. Andy Brehme

7. Czechoslovakia
8. Claudio Caniggia
9. Cameroon
10. John Barnes
11. Turin
12. Rudi Voller

13. Mick McCarthy
14. Stuart McCall
15. The United Arab Emirates
16. Nery Pumpido
17. Egypt
18. Michel

Sharp in the Box

Cameroon, Czechoslovakia, The Republic of Ireland and Yugoslavia

---

EUROPEAN CHAMPIONSHIP '88

1. Ireland
2. Marco Van Basten
3. AC Milan
4. Munich's Olympic Stadium
5. Ray Houghton
6. Erwin and Ronald Koeman

7. Denmark
8. Gianluca Vialli
9. Celtic
10. Igor Belanov
11. Arnold Muhren
12. Kenny Sansom

13. England
14. They were superstitious about changing after winning their first match while wearing white
15. Michel Vautrot
16. They were both substitutes
17. Scotland's
18. Dynamo Kiev

Sharp in the Box

Cologne, Dusseldorf, Frankfurt, Gelsenkirchen, Hamburg, Hannover and Stuttgart

---

ANSWERS TO QUIZ 22
WORLD CUP QUALIFYING

1. Norway
2. Italy
3. Germany and the USA
4. Israel
5. Jock Stein
6. Sweden

7. Dwight Yorke
8. El Salvador and Honduras
9. 1978
10. Spain
11. England
12. Mo Johnston

13. Albania
14. Puerto Rico
15. Jan Tomaszewski
16. New Zealand
17. Kevin Wilson
18. The USSR

Sharp in the Box

Belgium, Cyprus, Czechoslovakia, Faroe Islands and Romania

ANSWERS TO QUIZ 23
BEST OF BRITISH

1. 1982
2. Ryan Giggs
3. Navy blue
4. Billy Bingham
5. Ian Rush
6. 1958

7. Sweden
8. Brazil
9. Terry Neill
10. 1974
11. Peter Nicholas
12. Colin Clarke's

13. Brighton
14. Ally McLeod
15. 1976
16. 37
17. Colin Stein
18. Norman Whiteside

Sharp in the Box

Mike Smith, Mike England and David Williams (caretaker)

WORLD CUP PAST HISTORY

1. Brazil
2. Argentina
3. Paolo Rossi
4. Portugal
5. Johan Cruyff
6. 0-0

7. Carlos Alberto
8. The 1982 tournament
9. Jimmy Greaves
10. Paul Breitner
11. 1990
12. Jairzinho (Brazil)

13. 1950
14. Italy
15. Rene Van der Kerkhof
16. 1970
17. England and Brazil
18. 'Bulldog Bobby'

Sharp in the Box

Czechoslovakia, Hungary, Sweden, West Germany, Italy and Holland

---

ANSWERS TO QUIZ 25
THE MANAGERS

1. Ossie Ardilles
2. Oldham
3. Jim Smith
4. Derby County
5. Howard Wilkinson
6. Malcolm Crosby

7. Dave Bassett
8. QPR
9. Notts County
10. Luigi
11. Phil Neal
12. Kevin Keegan

13. Matt Busby
14. Alan Mullery
15. Chris McMenemy (Chesterfield)
16. Tommy Burns
17. Eoin Hand
18. Southampton

Sharp in the Box

Lincoln City, Watford and Aston Villa

ANSWERS TO QUIZ 26
HAVE BOOTS WILL TRAVEL

1. Chelsea
2. Marco Gabbiadini
3. Clive Allen
4. Paul Gascoigne
5. Northern Ireland
6. Alan Ball

7. John Gidman
8. Chelsea
9. Steve Hodge
10. Steve Archibald
11. Derby
12. Gillingham and Norwich

13. Spurs
14. Steve Daley
15. 15
16. Huddersfield Town
17. Gordon Smith
18. Three months

Sharp in the Box

Sunderland, Manchester City, Werder Bremen and Southampton

THE FOREIGN LEGION

1. Eric Cantona
2. Jan Molby
3. The CIS
4. Mirandinha
5. QPR and West Ham
6. Glenn Hysen

7. Arnold Muhren (1983)
8. Cremonese
9. Roland Nilsson
10. Birmingham City
11. Bert Trautmann
12. Frans Thijssen

13. Czechoslovakia's
14. Peter Ndlovu
15. He was one of the two Argentinians sent off in the World Cup Final
16. Ceri Evans
17. Preben Arentoft
18. Max Seeburg

Sharp in the Box

Craig Johnston and Bruce Grobbelaar

EARLY EXCHANGES

1. Bryan Robson
2. France
3. Holland
4. Vinny Jones
5. Clive Allen
6. Four seconds

7. Liam O'Brien
8. Steve Bould
9. Newcastle
10. Bryan Robson
11. Scotland
12. Yugoslavia

13. Alan McLoughlin
14. Ten seconds
15. Johnny Rep
16. Rangers and Hearts
17. Tommy Lawton
18. Nandor Hidegkuti

Sharp in the Box

Italy, West Germany (twice), Brazil (twice) and England

---

1. Yes
2. Four
3. Yes, but only if the ball has touched the goalkeeper before he strikes it again
4. Ten
5. No
6. 12 yards

7. False, there is no limit
8. There is no signal for a direct free-kick, only for an indirect one
9. No, he can only *signal* that a player, in his opinion, is in a offside position
10. The referee is unlikely to allow this since it constitutes an unnecessary danger to opponents
11. False, the other players need only be outside the penalty-area
12. He is signalling that a substitution is required

13. A direct free-kick from the place where the attacker was standing
14. Yes
15. Yes, any player may change places with the goalkeeper providing the referee is informed and the game is stopped
16. No, unless he considers that there was any attempt to deceive an opponent
17. 120 x 80 yards (110 x 75 metres)
18. Law 17 (corner-kick)

Sharp in the Box

Handling the ball plus striking, holding or pushing an opponent

---

---

1. Martin Keown
2. Bristol City
3. Pele
4. Italy
5. The League Championship, the Milk (League) Cup and the European Cup
6. Wallace

7. Emilio Butragueno
8. Hibs, Hearts and Meadowbank Thistle
9. Denis Law, Bobby Charlton and George Best
10. Celtic and Rangers
11. Cameroon and Italy
12. Bayern Munich, Borussia Moenchengladbach and Hamburg SV

13. Aston Villa
14. Tony Adcock, Paul Stewart and David White
15. 1981
16. Neuchatel Xamax
17. 1977
18. Alfredo di Stefano

Sharp in the Box

George Cohen, Jack Charlton, Bobby Moore and Ray Wilson

DRAMATIC DEBUTS

---

1. Alan Shearer
2. Manchester City
3. Graeme Souness
4. Jimmy Greaves
5. Scotland
6. True – he netted with a header

7. Six
8. Denis Law
9. Arsenal
10. Mark Hughes
11. Tony Coton
12. Romania

13. Leicester
14. Six seconds
15. Derby County
16. Paul Goddard
17. Torino
18. Allan Clarke (1970)

Sharp in the Box

Dalian Atkinson, Cyrille Regis and Steve Staunton

SUPER SUBS

1. The 1989 Final
2. Ian Rush
3. Stuart McCall
4. Roger Milla
5. Crystal Palace
6. Johan Cruyff

7. Mark Robins
8. Arsenal
9. 1982 (Altobelli of Italy)
10. David Fairclough
11. George Graham
12. Joe Jordan

13. Ralph Coates
14. Albania
15. Dirk Nanninga (for Holland in 1978)
16. John Hewitt
17. Glenn Hoddle and Mark Chamberlain
18. Hungary

Sharp in the Box

Hodge, McAllister, Whitlow, Shutt, Agana, Newsome and Cantona

QUITE A SEASON – 1991-92

1. Arsenal
2. Poland
3. Genoa
4. Bryan Robson
5. Crystal Palace's Ron Noades
6. West Ham

7. Dale Gordon
8. They lost 7-4 to Crewe
9. Anders Limpar
10. West Bromwich Albion
11. Tommy Coyne
12. Steve Hodge

13. Dennis Bailey
14. John Salako
15. United won both matches – 2-0 (home) and 3-1 (away)
16. Richard Gough
17. Manchester City
18. Frank McAvennie

Sharp in the Box

Ray Harford, Peter Withe and Joe Kinnear

ROUND THE GROUNDS

1. Stamford Bridge
2. Sheffield Wednesday
3. Hampden Park
4. Charlton Athletic
5. Wembley
6. False, there is a nearby cricket ground of the same name

7. Berwick Rangers
8. Wimbledon
9. Portman Road
10. Cleethorpes
11. Highbury
12. Middlesbrough, because their own ground had been closed due to the club's financial difficulties

13. Selhurst Park
14. The Olympic Stadium, Munich
15. They are all named after an individual
16. Liverpool's
17. Wigan Athletic
18. Molineux (Wolves)

Sharp in the Box

Celtic Park, Meadowbank Stadium and St Mirren Park

ANSWERS TO QUIZ 35
QUITE A SEASON 1990-91

---

1. Manchester United and Arsenal
2. Graeme Souness
3. Diego Maradona
4. Terry Butcher
5. Alan Hansen
6. Aberdeen

7. Bobby Robson
8. Luton
9. Everton and Liverpool
10. Hungary
11. Dennis Wise
12. The USSR and Argentina

13. Chelsea
14. Tony Gale
15. Wrexham
16. Derby
17. Their team bus was wheel-clamped and towed away
18. Their two groundsmen!

Sharp in the Box

Cambridge, Southend and Grimsby

ON THE SPOT

1. Liverpool, in 1992
2. On the goal-line between the posts
3. Red Star Belgrade
4. Jimmy Greaves
5. Manchester City
6. 1974's

7. Anton Rogan
8. Bournemouth
9. John Fashanu
10. Four
11. Kevin Reeves
12. Luton's Andy Dibble

13. They had lost the previous season's play-off Final in exactly the same manner
14. The penalty-spot had been obliterated and so the groundsman had to measure out and paint a new one
15. Robbie Resenbrink
16. Tony Parks
17. Andy Brehme
18. 20-19

Sharp in the Box

Romania, Yugoslavia, Italy and England

ANSWERS TO QUIZ 37
QUITE A SEASON 1989-90

1. The promotion play-offs
2. Safety at football grounds
3. Roberto Baggio
4. BSB
5. Mo Johnston
6. Swindon Town

7. Old Trafford
8. Trevor Francis (for QPR)
9. Bristol
10. Crystal Palace
11. Uruguay
12. Ajax Amsterdam

13. Millwall
14. Mick Quinn
15. The Welsh Cup
16. Stoke City
17. Aldershot 0 Sheffield Wednesday 8
18. FC Liege

Sharp in the Box

Kenny Dalglish (Liverpool), Graham Taylor (Aston Villa) and Terry Venables (Spurs)

RECORD BREAKERS

1. Pat Jennings
2. Spurs
3. Kenny Dalglish
4. Manchester City
5. Norman Whiteside
6. Walter Zenga

7. Coventry City
8. Kevin Francis
9. Gordon Strachan
10. 13
11. John Aldridge
12. Albion Rovers

13. Dixie Dean
14. 101
15. Austria v Hungary
16. Southend
17. Maine Road
18. Artur Friedenreich

Sharp in the Box

Alf Common, David Jack and Denis Law

QUITE A SEASON 1988-89

1. AC Milan
2. Alan Smith
3. Brian Clough
4. Celtic
5. Colin Moynihan
6. Chelsea

7. QPR
8. Vinny Jones
9. Hearts
10. Tony Cottee
11. Aston Villa
12. Luton

13. The USSR
14. Celtic
15. Paul Davis
16. George Best
17. Norwich
18. Arsenal and Manchester United

Sharp in the Box

England 0 Chile 0, Scotland 0 England 2, Scotland 2 Chile 0

SOCCER THE WORLD GAME

1. The African Nations Cup
2. Roy Wegerle
3. The World Club Championship match
4. It will be the first-ever indoor stadium used in the World Cup finals
5. North Korea
6. Abedi Pele

7. The Copa America
8. Australia, New Zealand and Malaysia
9. Ecuador
10. China
11. 1982
12. Colo Colo

13. Flamengo and Fluminese
14. Ghana
15. Tab Ramos
16. FAR
17. Colombia
18. Tony Waiters

Sharp in the Box

The United Arab Emirates and South Korea

THE CHAMPIONS' CUP

1. Manchester United
2. Wembley
3. Barcelona and PSV Eindhoven
4. Chris Waddle
5. Sparta Prague
6. Rome

7. Red Star Belgrade
8. 1987 (Bayern Munich v Porto)
9. Vujadin Boskov
10. Benfica
11. Trevor Francis
12. Bayern Munich (1974)

13. Kevin Campbell
14. Miodrag Belodedic
15. Ernst Happel
16. Dynamo Kiev
17. Karl Marx Stadt
18. Ferenc Puskas (Real Madrid v Benfica 1962)

Sharp in the Box

AC Milan, Manchester United, Ajax, Liverpool and Barcelona

FUTBOL ESPAÑOL

1. Johan Cruyff
2. Hugo Sanchez
3. Barcelona
4. Red
5. John Toshack
6. The Nou Camp

7. Robert Prosinecki
8. Tenerife
9. Real Sociedad
10. Carlos Valderrama
11. Chamartin
12. Jock Wallace

13. Athletic Bilbao
14. Valencia
15. Abel Resino
16. Seville
17. Luis Suarez
18. Castilla

Sharp in the Box

Barcelona, Real Madrid and Atletico Madrid

STARS OF EUROPE

1. Lothar Matthaus
2. Franco Baresi
3. Denmark
4. Hristo Stoichkov
5. Eintracht Frankfurt
6. 1984

7. Enzo Scifo
8. Soren Lerby
9. VfB Stuttgart
10. Anatoli Bishovets
11. Switzerland
12. Eric Gerets

13. Olympiakos
14. Heinz Hermann
15. Thomas Ravelli
16. Romania
17. Rudi Krol
18. Emil Kostadinov

Sharp in the Box

Gerd Muller, Franz Beckenbauer, Karl-Heinz Rummenigge
and Lothar Matthaus

THE CUP-WINNERS' CUP

1. Alex Ferguson
2. Werder Bremen
3. Gianluca Vialli
4. Ajax
5. Atletico Madrid
6. Mark Hughes

7. Moscow Dynamo
8. Johnny Metgod (for Feyenoord)
9. Lisbon
10. Wynton Rufer
11. Anderlecht
12. 10-1 to Monaco

13. Wolves
14. GKS Katowice
15. Gordon Durie
16. West Ham
17. Anderlecht, in 1978
18. FC Bruges

Sharp in the Box

Andy Gray, Trevor Steven and Kevin Sheedy

ANSWERS TO QUIZ 45
CALCIO THE ITALIAN LEAGUE

1. They became the first team to win the Championship without losing a match
2. Sampdoria
3. Roma
4. Rome
5. Juventus
6. Foreign players

7. Gianfranco Zola
8. Parma
9. Karl heinz Riedle and Thomas Doll
10. Inter Milan
11. Genoa
12. Giovanni Trapattoni

13. Cagliari
14. Gordon Cowans and Paul Rideout
15. The League Champions and the Cup holders
16. AC Milan's
17. Napoli (in 1987)
18. He was their goalkeeper who had ventured upfield for a last-minute corner

---

Sharp in the Box

Fiorentina, AC Milan, Inter Milan, Juventus, Roma and Sampdoria

---

THE UEFA CUP

1. Ajax Amsterdam
2. It is played over two 'home-and-away' legs
3. Ipswich and Spurs
4. Dundee United
5. England's
6. Bill Shankly

7. Walter Casagrande
8. IFK Gothenburg
9. Belgium
10. Dean Saunders
11. VfB Stuttgart
12. John Wark (Ipswich)

13. The International Inter-City Industrial Fairs Cup
14. Rafael Martin-Vazquez
15. Bayer Leverkusen
16. Mike Belfield (for Finnish side Kuusysi Lahti)
17. Real Madrid (1985 and 1986)
18. Juventus (they lost the Final to Leeds on 'away goals')

Sharp in the Box

Ajax, Barcelona and Juventus

ANSWERS TO QUIZ 47
THE FRENCH CONNECTION

1. £5 million
2. Monaco
3. Bernard Tapie
4. The Parc des Princes, Paris
5. Scotland
6. Bastia, in Corsica

7. Nantes
8. Portugal
9. St Etienne
10. Graham Rix
11. Montpellier
12. 1988

13. Tomislav Ivic
14. The Ivory Coast
15. Metz
16. Manual Amoros
17. Paris St Germain
18. The Stade Louis II in Monaco

Sharp in the Box

Stade de Reims, St Etienne and Marseille

CONTINENTAL HIT-MEN

1. Adidas
2. 'Toto'
3. Jean-Pierre Papin
4. 'Der Bomber'
5. Marco Van Basten
6. Darko Pancev

7. Ajax
8. CSKA Sofia
9. Mixu Paatelainen
10. Anderlecht
11. Jan Ceulemans
12. Stefan Pettersson

13. Horst Hrubesch
14. Ruud Gullit
15. Eintracht Frankfurt
16. Toni Polster
17. Tanju Colak
18. It was revealed that he had been a spy for the *Stasi* (secret police) under the old East German regime

---

Sharp in the Box

Bobby Lennox, Joe Harper and Charlie Nicholas

SPORTING SOCCER FANS

1. Seve Ballesteros
2. Everton
3. Liz McColgan
4. Chelsea
5. Steve Cram
6. Steven Hendry

7. Crystal Palace
8. Graham Gooch
9. Coventry City
10. Chelsea
11. He's a Charlton fan
12. Julian Wilson

13. Wolves
14. Jonathan Davies
15. Celtic
16. Manchester United
17. Leeds
18. John McCririck

Sharp in the Box

Robbie Brightwell and Ann Packer

ANSWERS TO QUIZ 50
READ ALL ABOUT IT

1. *Shoot!*
2. Steve Bull
3. Arsenal
4. Germany
5. Jimmy Greaves
6. Goalkeepers

7. *Viz*
8. *Rangers News*
9. Brian Glanville
10. Alan Rough
11. Bobby Robson's
12. Spain

13. Spurs in European competition
14. Charles Hughes
15. Port Vale
16. Arsenal's Irish players
17. *La Gazzetta dello Sport*
18. *Hampden Babylon*

Sharp in the Box

It's a play on words referring to the fans' song 'Wen…dy Saints, go marching in…'

HOWZAT! FOOTBALLING CRICKETERS

1. Viv Richards
2. Andy Goram
3. Scunthorpe
4. Geoff Hurst
5. Mike Gatting
6. The Oval

7. Denis Compton
8. Jim Cumbes
9. Brian Close
10. Ted Drake
11. Bramall Lane (home of Sheffield United)
12. Chris Morris'

13. Charlton
14. Phil Neale
15. Scot Symon
16. Chris Balderstone
17. Tim Buzaglo
18. Hamilton Crescent

Sharp in the Box

In olden days, a bowler who took three consecutive wickets was rewarded with a new hat

---

ANSWERS TO QUIZ 52
THE COLOURS

---

1. Red
2. Claret and blue
3. QPR
4. Blue
5. Both did!
6. Hibs and Celtic

7. Leeds
8. White shirts with navy blue shorts
9. Umbro
10. Red and yellow
11. Arsenal's
12. Black and white

13. No. 3
14. Yellow
15. Albion Rovers
16. They wore white jerseys in the first half and (on the instructions of the referee) blue in the second
17. Green, black and white
18. Swopping jerseys

Sharp in the Box

White, red, sky blue and yellow

---

1. Bill Shankly
2. Vinny Jones
3. Ron Atkinson
4. Nigel's mum
5. Ally McCoist
6. Jasper Carrott

7. Stan Boardman
8. Alex Ferguson
9. John Aldridge
10. Len Shackleton
11. Don Howe
12. Mick McCarthy

13. Dave Bassett
14. 'See one wall and you've seen them all'
15. Jimmy Greaves
16. He said that it would ruin his Saturday nights
17. John Motson
18. Alex Ferguson

Sharp in the Box

Tommy Docherty

THE SONG REMAINS THE SAME

1. 'You'll Never Walk Alone'
2. New Order
3. Luciano Pavarotti
4. 'Abide With Me'
5. West Ham's
6. Ossie Ardiles

7. 'Elland Road is the only place for us'
8. Portsmouth's
9. 'Guantanamera'
10. 'When The Year Ends In One'
11. Eric Idle
12. 'Goodnight Irene'

13. 'Glad All Over'
14. Paul Heaton
15. Celtic's
16. He is a Manchester United fan
17. 'Careless Hands'
18. John Robertson

Sharp in the Box

Steve Archibald

SOCCER ON THE BOX

1. *Match of the Day*
2. Trevor Brooking
3. Liverpool
4. Arsenal
5. Kenneth Wolstenholme's
6. BBC

7. Martin Tyler
8. Kevin Keegan
9. Screensport
10. Ian Botham (he played football too, remember!)
11. Barry Davies
12. Wycombe Wanderers

13. 1954
14. Simon O'Brien
15. Boston United
16. Jock Brown
17. Mick Robinson
18. 20

Sharp in the Box

Scotland, England, Italy and Germany

ANSWERS TO QUIZ 56
STRANGE BUT TRUE?

---

1. True (Allan Hansen of Odense BK)
2. Kenny Dalglish
3. True (Richard Gough)
4. Everton
5. True (Princess Alexandra, wife of Edward *VII*)
6. Boris Becker

7. Stan Bowles
8. That year's competition was played on a two-leg basis
9. Jimmy Sandison
10. Vic Halom
11. Alex Stepney
12. Malta

13. Seven
14. Their head of state had threatened to execute them if they played badly!
15. Cowdenbeath
16. Four
17. To combat floodlight glare
18. A dog which ran onto the field and tackled him

Sharp in the Box

Neville Southall (1985), Clive Allen (1987) and John Barnes (1988)
